JOURNEYS WITH ANUBIS

A Woman's Initiation into Ancient Egypt

SUSANNE E. STEINEL

Journeys with Anubis

A Woman's Initiation into Ancient Egypt

By Susanne E. Steinel

Susanne E. Steinel/Murannah
Brunnenstrasse 166
10119 Berlin
Germany
Email: susanne.steinel@me.com
www.murannah.house

ISBN: 978-3-9818389-0-9

Cover Designed by Csaba Dzsurnik

To the ones

who love and support us

—always.

To the ones

who live this life

gently.

CONTENTS

1

THE STRANGER

He'd never said a word when he accompanied her on those first trips. Maybe he knew he would scare her off, make her run away, run to the end of the world and drop off at the ridge, right into the abyss. Maybe he'd been waiting for her to make the first move, a move which would have indicated a victory of her curiosity and trust over her fear. He never said a word on those first trips.

Silently, he stood at the other end of this long, canoe-like boat, an erect figure in a dark cape, his head buried in a black cloth. He held a long stick in his hand which he used to steer the boat across the gray lake. His movements were precise, never hurried, always serene. He seemed to be moving in slow motion. He was a complete stranger to her, yet the more often she went down there, down into that cave, the more she trusted him, his sheer presence, his beingness, his being there. It seemed he was the only real being down there besides her.

She was relieved that he had never turned his face. She was also dimly aware of the anxiety within her, a snake-like energy which never left her completely. She would have freaked out, indeed, if her eyes had fallen on those animal features which the teacher had described to his audience as a jackal head on top of an otherwise human corpse. No way could she imagine glancing at his face in those first days of encounters, not down there in this boat, in the dark, somewhere in the womb of this planet.

Still, she was extremely grateful he was there. She didn't doubt that if he had not been there, if he had not been introduced to her as a trustworthy companion on her voyage into her own underworld, she would never have set foot on those declining stairs into the earth, would never have walked to that lake in the dim light of this giant underground cave, would never have climbed into this elongated and slender wooden boat.

Anubis had been introduced to her at a sound-healer seminar, the first of a series of seminars. The teacher, back then only reasonably renowned, had introduced Anubis to his audience. He had actually invoked this ancient Egyptian deity with his voice through a spiralling and deeply moving sound meditation which would shift the whole group—so he had explained later—into an altered state of consciousness. At the end of the seminar, the sound healer had encouraged them all to call Anubis whenever they meditated and explored their own underworld. He had slightly laughed at his own words but then had added in a matter-of-fact voice that this being would always be a faithful companion. "Always," he had repeated in a dark tone.

Not much later, after her first encounters with this stranger and her own past, her present, and indeed potential future, she got to know his story—the story of the Egyptian god, the wounded shaman, the one who knows from his heart what it means to be an abandoned child. At first, she had no idea why she had been drawn particularly to him rather than to any of the other Egyptian deities. Gradually, she began to understand: he was the initiator, the way-shower, the one who heals and teaches from the beginning of times up until now and way into the future.

* * *

"I live an ordinary life," she repeated, more vigorously this time while pouring more Coke into her glass. Her face was flushed. The two young women sat on Clara's sofa in her living room, high up above the roofs in Munich. They were in the midst of one of their usual arguments about their lifes' purposes, their desperate and not-so-desperate struggles with the other half of the human gender, and their latest twists and turns in their plans and dreams.

Both women were in their late twenties and quite different in their appearances, like salt and pepper, as some of their joint acquaintances would say. Clara was average-sized and slim. Her usually pale face was enframed by black, curly hair and dominated by huge, dark eyes. She used to have the look of a lost girl, but since she'd befriended Erna, it had changed into a somewhat elfish expression she could switch on and off when she wished to. She loved to wear long skirts, and her favorite one had big, red roses printed on a dark green background.

Erna, on the contrary, had fair hair and a boyish haircut. She was boisterous with a fiery temperament, always ready for a good laugh or a walk on the wild side, as she would call it. She was considerably smaller than Clara, but no one could tell, as she always stood straight. She was full of energy and quite sinewy, and her whole body seemed to constantly be on the move. It was as if she vibrated at a frequency at least an octave higher than Clara's.

They first met at a dinner party in the frame of a business conference organised by the ICM, the International Congress Center of Munich. Both woman were in charge of several of their agency´s clients and their respective marketing activities at the conference. Both of them were equally bored by the stiffness and the artificiality of the event and the conversations.

When they stood in the queue to get themselves a drink, they immediately clicked, and within no time, they started tittering and forgot all about their responsibilities. It was good that the conference had come to an end by then. Their employers would not have appreciated their lack of concern regarding their respective clients.

"I am as ordinary as a young woman could be," Clara now protested.

Erna chuckled and waved her hands theatrically as she spoke. "Clara! There is no such person as a *normal* person! You have been made from two very succinct and unique human beings. You carry within your DNA the lineage of many very different former life times. The constellations of the stars at your birth were as never before and after. And see how you live!"

Erna threw her arms into the air in a wide circle. "Look at all those crystals in the corner and the wild orange painting by this Australian aboriginal woman with all those symbols nobody in this part of the world can decipher. Look at this phenomenal bright pink carpet on the ground. And this huge poster of the neon-green bat hanging down from the half-broken iron rod of its cage. Your life is full of color, full of mystery, full of questions. How could you possibly say you are a normal woman!"

Clara blinked.

"And also . . ." Erna's expression conjured dismay, "also, if you think *you* are a normal woman, you are degrading me—me!—your one and only, best, most exceptional girlfriend!" She lowered her head and whispered conspiratorially. "And believe me, my dear, I am extraordinary. I know it!"

Erna grunted, popped some dried mango pieces in her mouth, and began to vigorously chew. Then she bent over and gave Clara a little exalted kiss on her cheek.

Clara stretched her bare legs and rubbed her ankles; they ached from when she and Erna had their extensive shopping tour in hot downtown Munich. The mid-summer sun had burned down on Germany, and indeed the whole of Europe, for the last five weeks. There had not been a single drop of rain. How Clara longed for autumn! The heat made her dizzy and feeble.

Erna, in contrast, did not seem to be much affected by it. She had just thrown several bags of new clothes onto the sofa, extremely content with her new purchases, and was now rummaging through them with much delight.

Clara had not been in the mood for major investments. She had only bought some socks for the gym and a light scarf. With a strained face, she massaged her feet.

"I know, I know." Even her voice sounded weary. "I am hearing this from you again and again," Clara then murmured. "Your words put me under pressure. It is as if I have a mission to fulfill, a holy mission, and I have no idea what to preach."

With a tantalizing smile, Erna started tapping her feet like a tap dancer. "What about becoming enlightened?" she sang, stretching her arms to the right and left. "What about the two of us becoming one blazing ball of light, wuuuh . . . aaaah . . . wonderfuuuul!"

Erna stopped swirling and cast a serious look at Clara. "Enlightenment in the sense of *ecstasy*, of course. We do not want a boring void! We want ecstasy of the heart and soul! Yes, that is what we want!"

And with those words, she began to swirl around again, a celestial expression on her face.

Clara gave her a sceptical look. "Sounds simple."

"It is simple!" Erna retorted. "Ask this guy you have been talking about, the guy down there at the cave! He should know, eh? What is his name? Anubis? Isn't he some sort of a god, no?"

She spun around again, into the direction of the kitchen. "I take another Coke from the fridge, may I?"

Before Clara could answer, Erna disappeared behind the kitchen door.

"Of course you may," Clara mumbled to herself.

They definitely had their rituals when together, and drinking ridiculous amounts of Coke was one of them. Clara sighed and put her legs on the small table in front of her. Oh, what heaven! She could not recall a moment when she had not enjoyed Erna's company, and deep in her heart, she knew how lucky she was to have her as a friend.

* * *

Clara remembered her return from the first sound-healing workshop as if it were yesterday. She had stepped up the stairs to the sixth floor and had entered her reclusive apartment located at the top of one of the few beautiful art-nouveau buildings of Schwabing, the buzzing student area of Munich. It had been built at the turn of the last century and had escaped, by sheer chance, the destructive bombs of World War II. The houses left and right to her building were from the fifties, concrete blocks without much charm.

Dropping her bags and her suitcase in the corridor, Clara went across her living room to her king size bed with its heavy Indian multicolored bedspread. She sat down on her bed with her back against the wall and folded her hands. Then she closed her eyes.

Would she have the courage to summon him? Would she dare say his name, invoke his presence and ask him to accompany her down to that cave? Why should she, anyway? Who was she to call a being like him?

The very moment she had finished this trail of thought, she felt a powerful and distinct shift of energy in her room. The tiny hair on her skin rose, and a wavelike tremor coursed through her whole body.

"Are you there?" she asked with a hushed voice.

Come down to the lake, she heard him say, though there was not a single sound in the room. His voice came from afar—and at the same time, it echoed from a place deep inside her.

Those words—*Come down to the lake*—marked the beginning of

Clara's intimate conversations with Anubis. From then on, whenever she felt the calling, she walked down those imaginary stairs to meet him at the lake. She found him there, always. She would pour out her heart and give birth to questions that were unknown to her until that very moment when she sat down on the wooden bench of his boat.

"What is your role in this?"

It was one of her first questions, and he had answered her calmly.

"I am steering you safely across this lake."

She had leaned back against the plank of the bench and closed her eyes. His voice echoed in her heart.

I am steering you safely across this lake.

It was not the answer she had anticipated.

It was an answer, however, which fulfilled her deeply. Her body flooded with a profound sensation of being taken care of, and she relaxed into this unfamiliar feeling. Whoever he was, whatever she might experience here in this strangely intimate place—which she gradually came to understand was her own underworld—his tranquility engulfed her. And although she experienced utter peacefulness at that moment, some parts of her remained on alert. She felt no traces of fatigue, no endeavor within her to give over the reins to him. Somehow Clara understood that it was her responsibility to face whatever might come up from the depths of this sea of her own unconsciousness. She was not to give this responsibility over to him.

With his sheer presence, he created a safe space for whatever she chose to experience. He was there to provide a reflection. However, it was up to her to explore its truth. It was entirely up to her to face the pains and joys of living on this planet called Earth.

* * *

"Will you join me for a visit to the new Egyptian museum?" she had asked Erna the other day on the phone.

Erna had declined. She had been unusually elliptical, and Clara did not want to squeeze her. When she decided to go alone, her stomach tightened. A sense of foreboding filled her, and she quickly pushed it away. She was determined to go.

The museum had only opened a few weeks earlier, and its architecture had been branded as spectacular. When Clara escaped the Underground and stepped into full daylight, she squinted her eyes. The tall, four-sided building stood right in front of her. Flat, wide stretching steps of light-gray stone traced down and away from the busy street, leading to a gigantic wall with a small, quadrangular entrance. The size and shape of the wall's concrete blocks reminded her of the blocks of the Egyptian pyramids. The illusion of approaching one of those ancient pyramids was nearly perfect. With each step Clara took, the pandemonium of the city receded into the background. The walls to the left and right, as well as the giant wall in front of Clara, began to enclose her. The light faded away, although it was midday and the sun had just crossed its highest point at the horizon.

When Clara stood in front of the entrance door, it surprised her that the door was actually oversized, taller than average. The entrance had seemed so tiny from above!

She reached out for the massive metal handgrip and tore open the door. *This building demands respect*, she thought, shuddering, and she entered in awe. When she heard the door fall back behind her, she breathed in deeply. It was so dark inside! Slowly, her eyes adjusted to the dim light. She stood in a large hall with a reception table to her right, where tickets were sold. The entire left side of the hall was a glass front with an almost invisible glass door—the entrance to the exhibition itself.

Had it been that dark in the pyramids? How were they able to see?

Clara crammed her coat and bag into one of the nearby lockers and went to buy the ticket. A desk officer offered her a device that would allow a tour guide to give her information as she walked around.

"No, thank you. No media devices," she said to the desk officer, shaking her head. Those scholarly voices would only confuse her. Her intuition would hopefully lead her to those pieces of information which were of relevance to her.

She went through the glass door and down another flight of stairs into the ground. The ceilings of the rooms situated below earth-level were very high, at least four times her size. There were concrete pillars everywhere, engraved all over with Egyptian symbols and hieroglyphs, and the resemblance to the pillars of the temples of Luxor and other Egyptian sites she had seen on photos was striking.

The dreamlike atmosphere mesmerized Clara. She had the strange impression that her skin was expanding and soaking up the information captured in the forms, colors, and muffled sounds around her. Her mind gave up its usual chatter. When she saw the adhesive tape on the ground indicating to visitors the way through the various exhibition rooms, she slowly followed it. She felt like an animal sniffing its way through an alien and yet strangely familiar world. All her senses were highly activated. She trusted that her body knew how to take in the vibrations of those mysterious artifacts: those life-sized statues of Egyptian gods and goddesses, those breathtaking solid heads of priests and priestesses, and also the precious frailty of the jewelry and those miniature vessels.

When she ventured around a sharp corner, her eyes hit a carved head in brown quartzite stabbed on a metal rod atop a concrete pillar.

It was a man's head, and his stony eyes were exactly at her eye level. They looked directly into hers with such unflinching vividness that she shrank back and tumbled.

She closed her eyes for a second. When she opened them, she found herself again in the focus of his eyes. It was as if he was looking into her—looking *through* her—way into her past. His eyes expressed humility and power at the same time.

I know this man so well!

Yet his stony eyes did not reveal anything to her.

Who was he?

She bent her head to decipher what was written on the tiny metal plate. *Head from a block statue of a priest in Egypt, 650 B.C.*

A woman came around the corner and Clara noticed that she, too, was drawn to the priest's striking head. The woman moved closer, but then she turned abruptly and hurried away with a frightened expression on her face.

Puzzled about her sudden flight, Clara moved back to the head and concentrated again on his face. All at once, a sentence flashed in her head: *Move into my head.*

She winced. *What was that? Where did the sentence come from?* Nervously, she began to withdraw from the statue. Then she froze. *Had the spotlight just lit up his head? What an obscure suggestion to move into someone's head! How could that be possible, anyway?*

The very moment she finished that line of thought, she noticed a palpable jerk. It sounded as if one of her spinal vertebras had snapped into a new place. *What was going on here?*

There was no doubt: she had moved into another place, and this place felt more vast, but at the same time, more solid. A soft, brownish light glowed around her, which seemed impermeable to her. Where *was* she?

I bow down to you, she thought, much to her surprise. *I bow down to you, and I am honored to be with you.*

She could not question it anymore! Somehow she had moved inside this stony head.

Bewildered, she suddenly wondered, did I ask for permission? Is it important to ask for permission before doing such things? She remembered having read something along those lines. But then, had he not invited her?

I appreciate your wisdom, she heard herself thinking, as if the words were spoken aloud.

The atmosphere became intense. She did not know where to look. The brown impenetrable color still hovered around her. A sudden stirring occurred in the center of her chest. Something inside her opened up and widened. It was as if a small caldera had opened up, its rims stretching to all sides. It felt blissful, but there was also pain at the edges, as if a delicate membrane had been torn so much that it threatened to rip. She closed her eyes for a moment. Never before had she experienced such a strange mixture of opening up, of bliss and pain at the same time.

I am bathing in pure love, she realized with surprise.

Finally, you came. Finally, we meet.

A tremendous tension built in her body. She so much enjoyed this bath of pure love, but then, it overwhelmed her, and pain still lingered at the edges. She became afraid.

Oh my God, she thought, where am I?

"Who are you?" she managed to ask silently.

The answer was clear. *You have known me since aeons. We met in the beginning of times. We worshipped the same gods and goddesses. We performed the same sacred rituals.*

I do not know you.

You are beginning to remember. His voice became more urgent in her head. *Remember, Murannah!*

Murannah? An electric jolt moved through her body, and she had the strange impression that her hair stood on her head in all directions. *Murannah!* Then there was movement in her head, and she felt as if she were being swirled around. Moments later, she found herself outside him again, right in front of that motionless face of his,

his eyes looking through her and into the far distance.

She felt dizzy. When she stepped back and stumbled, she noticed other visitors taking note of her strange behavior. She hastily gathered herself and moved away from him.

A Priest of Egypt.

The thought caused her to tremble. *What does a stone head of a priest of Egypt have to tell* me?

Suddenly, there was a shrill metal clang in the air, and all lights went out. Pitch blackness surrounded Clara, and even when her eyes had adjusted to the darkness, she could get hold of nothing—no lights, no shapes, nothing. The darkness was unpierceable. It jumped at her like a wild animal. She shuddered.

She heard exclamations of surprise from people around her, some cursing, and the sound of scuffling steps.

A man shouted tensely, "Hey, switch on the lights!"

There was the dull sound of a body hitting one of the glass vitrines.

Clara's throat tightened, and she gasped. She could not recall ever having experienced such bleak darkness in her life. The anxiety in the cacophony of voices around her increased. Someone or something lightly touched her left arm, and she frantically shrank away. Apparently, visitors were trying to make their way up to the stairs. Panicking, she stretched out both arms. *Don't you dare touch me*, she wanted to scream, but her voice cracked. She could only screech, "Hello?" Her voice sounded unfamiliarly harsh. "Anybody here?"

For a brief moment, she caught the faint scent of something unfamiliar to her—something animal-like. She shivered. She had no idea where to go. In that darkness, she might even travel in circles without noticing it. *Why don't they fix the lights, for heaven's sake?*

Desperately, Clara blinked, willing her eyes to see something, *anything*. It was futile. She saw nothing. The feeling of being swallowed by darkness increased. Her panic was creeping up her spine and into her head like a slow-moving vicious serpent. Silently she began to pray without really knowing who she was addressing. "Please," she murmured with a rasping voice. "Please."

Suddenly, she saw a strong white light directly in front of her. She stared at it in disbelief. It was as far away as the Egyptian priest's head. The light came from the place between his eyes, from the center of his forehead.

Move into my head, he said to her again.

There was a sharp, high-pitched buzzing sound. She had no time to think. Instantly, her head filled with white light. In the center of it, hovering in the air, hung a white crystal. It was as big as a fist, and it had a power, clarity, and beauty that took her breath away.

See the pulsation of its light, the voice said.

She stared at the crystal, and she quivered.

It was as if the crystal had breathed in the darkness and immediately flashed it out again in multiple rays of light. It seemed to be a pulsating, living thing, bathing the whole exhibition room in a surreal white light.

"Are you doing this?" she whispered in awe.

I am metabolizing light. You are metabolizing light.

"I do not understand," she murmured. A dull knocking sounded in her head.

It is a secret. A secret awaiting revelation. Soon, the time will come. You are on your path.

When she looked down, she sighed in relief. She could see clearly the tape on the ground. She knew she would be out of this room, out of this museum, soon. Slowly, she took a step, then another, following the tape. At that moment, the lights came on.

She turned back to look at his head, but his eyes were as

impenetrable as before.

She raised her right hand and shyly waved goodbye.

"I will come back," she whispered, and with a sudden urge to move onward, she headed towards the exit.

* * *

Clara roamed for him. She sat in front of her notebook screen for hours, searching the internet, keying in *Anubis* in many different variations and combinations, Anubis with *Egypt*, Anubis with *temple*, Anubis, Anubis, Anubis. There were many sources referring to other phenomena, not to the Egyptian god figure, nor Egyptian culture or spirituality. She became desperate, as traces were so thin or overly academic, transcriptions of hieroglyphs and copies of old scripts incomprehensible to her. At times she had the feeling he was standing behind her, looking over her shoulders, smiling, pointing at some outrageous piece of information while shaking his head in disbelief.

This is great fun, she thought she heard him say at some point. She turned around only to stare into the void, a void out of which she expected him to jump out like a phantom. *Here I am. Let us go out and have a pizza.*

Then, on one occasion, she clearly heard a voice say, *look at this!*

Her attention was drawn to a paragraph on Egyptian gods and goddesses as archetypes for different qualities. She read that they were worshipped in a time when the true power of the feminine and the masculine were equally celebrated.

She thought, how, for heaven's sake, should this work? As if she had voiced her question aloud, she heard a whisper.

This is the big secret, the gulden vlies, the sword and the holy grail. Are you ready to walk this path to your own enlightenment, I wonder, Clara? Are you ready to be dissolved into the light, as this is where this path might truly lead you to?

She laughed uneasily, trying to shake off her trepidation.

There is much ecstasy involved in this, he whispered inside her mind, *much ecstasy, but also pain, I warn you. Are you ready to walk this path with me?"*

"Is this a temptation?" she said out loud, her voice disrupting the silence like a whirlwind swirling leaves into the air.

There was no response. She sighed.

"Well, Anubis," she then said in a low voice, "if this is a serious offer, you will have to teach me a lot! The span of my lifetime might not be long enough to learn all this, and truly, you will have a difficult time convincing me that this man-woman dream will ever come true. I'd better tell you now."

As soon as she uttered her warning, she heard his silent laughter.

She sensed a movement beneath her, and then she felt his presence so strongly that she expected to see his outline.

Would he materialize here, in her flat, right beside her chair? She hoped not! She did not feel prepared at all for an encounter in this part of her world.

Resolutely, she switched off her computer.

"Finished for today!" she said aloud and stood.

* * *

She did not meditate for a whole week.

Something in her resisted going down that cave. Something in her hesitated. Too much to do, she kept telling herself. What might come up next? Then she began to doubt her sanity. Calling Anubis to accompany her into a cave somewhere in her own underworld . . . how more absurd could life become?

No, she definitely did *not* want to be drawn into all of that.

At the same time, she felt dispirited, as if depression loomed around the corner.

"You pretend he is not there," Erna told her on the phone. "You try to cheat yourself. It won´t work, I tell you."

"Oh, shut up," Clara said.

She was not ready to discuss her ambiguous feelings with Erna. If she were being honest, she would admit that she hoped her life would be normal again. Whatever *a normal life* meant. No weird travels into this cave, no bewildering explorations, no strange talks with this being who was said to be half-human, half-jackal. More than once, she caught herself staring at the notebook screen, dreading he would jump out of it. At the same time, she was silently wishing he would show up.

"Well, if I am to shut up, and you are to stay closed like a celibate oyster, we might as well just finish our call," Erna said with gaiety in her voice, and hung up.

"Oh, my dear friend," Clara mumbled into the dead phone. Then she sighed and hung up too. After all, Erna was right. There was no point in talking right now. She would need to figure out how she could get out of this depressive mood of hers first. Was her depression just a disguise for fearfulness? Her fear of entering a process that might change her more than she could imagine?

I am definitely afraid of losing control, she suddenly realized. *I might end up becoming schizophrenic!*

Clara was determined to do everything possible to steer her life back into calm waters.

* * *

Why are you hiding, Clara?

She swivelled around, gasping.

"Where are you?" she said loudly, staring into her living room. There was no trace of him, at least no trace visible to her.

You called me, he answered in her head.

"I did not!" The sharp sound of her voice cut through the air. She jolted backward.

Know that I never turn up, if not called. Never. I always respect your freewill.

Clara tilted her head. His voice was so pure and clear that she'd swear he was there in the room with her. The wind tore mercilessly at the windowpanes, but some minutes passed before he spoke again.

You have all the choices, Clara. You want me to leave again? I will leave.

The air stirred around her.

"No, no!" she said hastily. "Please stay."

What if I stay until you have made up your mind? I will hold the space while you contemplate this, okay?

She let out a relieved sigh. "Okay," she agreed.

Then she closed her eyes.

It calmed her to know he was there. His presence allowed her peacefulness, as if there was nothing she needed to do.

She suddenly thought, how long will you be here for me? It might take too long, this process of making up my mind. She nibbled a fingernail and shifted on her sofa.

Eternally.

Again, his answer was crisp and clear. *Know that I am used to waiting eternally. I will not abandon you. Take your aeons.*

"Take your aeons?" she asked, then giggled. "I will be an old granny then. No! Not even that! A grain of dust, or part of a spider's silken web!"

Just take this as a saying of an ancient being; I will not go away, until you clearly and willingly ask me so.

"Oh, good!" She dropped back into the sofa.

Silence settled in.

May I suggest something? he said after a while.

"Sure."

Ask a question!

Her mind went blank. What could she ask? Sure, he probably wanted her to ask about life and death, the really big questions. But Clara couldn't begin to voice those thoughts. It was too difficult to even find an entrance into those questions. They were like convoluted knots to her.

She rubbed her arms and swallowed hard. Was she really this stupid? Why couldn't she come up with an intelligent question? Her face grew warm. She couldn't string together a logical sentence.

Are you afraid of asking stupid questions? His voice softened. *Or are you afraid of the answers?*

"Both, I guess." Clara crossed her arms. "Also, I do not know where to start."

The act of asking demands great courage.

"Why is that? Why should it require courage?"

There are times when it is dangerous to ask questions.

Her stomach fluttered. "Dangerous?" How would she know when it was dangerous? Might it not be dangerous right now?

There are questions that could create too much attention by the ones in power. This attention could be lethal. The answers, too, in another way. You know this, because it is ingrained in your DNA. The hiding of questions and answers becomes extremely important, so you fall silent. Gradually you forget that, once, you wanted to know.

Clara pondered his words. She cast a look at the alarm clock at the right corner of her room. She had not seen the minute hand moving for quite some time now. Her blood curdled.

The hiding or suppression of questions absorbs a great deal of energy. When you grow up, you feel those wormholes where your questions and their answers hover like ghosts. You do not know how to make them your own. You feel overwhelmed. You might even feel depressed. Grasping even one of those ghosts and revealing its question can catapult you out of a depression in an instant.

"But how do I find the right question?" Clara asked.

It is both a process of stalking and of letting go. You must become receptive. When you realize the question hovering around you, you stalk it. At the same time, you open a space within yourself to let yourself be magnetised by it. It takes courage, Clara.

Once you have found the questions . . . .

When he didn't finish, Clara grew impatient. "What then? Do I need someone like you to get the answer?"

When the question is clear, the answer will come to you equally clearly. A true question always leads to a true answer.

Neither spoke for several minutes as Clara turned over his words in her head. When she finally spoke, her voice sounded tentative, even cautious. "I guess my question and my fear is whether I will lose my senses. I mean, will I become a lunatic by being with you? Or rather by you making yourself known . . . somehow . . ." she struggled to find the right words, "somehow within me?"

The moment she voiced her question, she knew the answer. Her entire body resonated with it. An exquisite sense of lucidity expanding from the center of her heart filled her entire being. Only her skin held it in, kept the lucidity from spilling out into the room.

His words echoed her knowledge. *I am called* The One Who

shows the Way to Enlightenment, *Clara. I am here to help you cut through the veil of ignorance. If you are ready to face your fears and release the blocks which impede you from walking your path of power, I am here to support you.*

Know that I honor your decision, always.

It might be this lifetime. It might be the next. It is always you who is in charge.

The air shifted around her, and she had the fleeting impression that he had just bowed down to her.

As I said, I am used to waiting.

After that, he grew quiet, and so did Clara. Then there was silence which she did not feel like interrupting for a long time.

2

THE WOUNDED SHAMAN

Clara let her hands drop into the clear, underground lakewater. The water remained calm, as usual, and a soft breeze gently stirred the leaves near the bushes along the shore.

"I did some research on your titles."

She gazed at her surroundings as the boat slowly glided across the smooth surface of the lake. Clara peered into the water. Were there any fish in there? She had not seen a single creature down here. It soothed her to think no fish swam here—better no life than a Loch Ness Monster or a great white shark with pointed teeth. She shuddered at the thought and withdrew her hands from the water.

She turned towards Anubis. "I've been researching, but the information I found is confusing. Some of the names you were given, I understand, such as *The Jackal Headed God* or *The Steersman of the Boat of Millions of Years*. After all," she said and shrugged, "this is what you do with me. You steer me over this lake, don't you? When I first met you, you were introduced to me as a guide into my own underworld. So I guess those titles refer to those features of yours." Clara tilted her head to one side. "But other titles are more difficult for me to grasp."

"Which ones?" he asked lightly, bending towards her but still looking out to the horizon. "I might be able to explain."

"Well, I also found *The Weigher of Hearts in the Halls of Amenti, the Mouth Opener,* and last but not least . . . . "

"Last but not least?" he repeated.

"Last but not least," Clara's voice softened, "I also found the name *The Wounded Shaman.*"

"You do not understand?"

"I always associated shamanism with Native American or Asian indigenous cultures, never with the ancient civilization of Egypt. Why would you possibly be called a *shaman*? And why *wounded*?"

"There is a sacred wound within each of us," Anubis said slowly. "When we heal this wound by embracing it and integrating the lessons that go with it, we are healing ourselves. We also contribute to the healings of others. A shaman has learnt how to move into the hidden side of things and retrieve from darkness the shaman's jewel—the jewel for manifesting healing. You are here because you want to know how to heal yourself."

Anubis fell silent for a moment. Then he said, "We share the same wound, Clara. It is the wound of abandonment and separation. Yours came with claustrophobia, because when the wound was cut, you could not escape. The memory of all this is still held in your cells."

Clara stared at him. His words rang as true in her body as the sound of a faraway bell. There was no association, however, with any images or feelings.

He tilted his head. "Remember, I am here to steer you safely over this lake. I know how to release those painful memories. There will be a time when this wound of yours will not influence your life anymore."

He gave his words a moment to sink in. "The scars will not stop vibrating. You will, however, stay strong in your own circle of power, and the wounds will no longer drive your actions in life or prevent you from understanding what you truly are."

Clara pondered his words for a few minutes before speaking. "What kind of sacred wounds are there?"

"There are many. You know them all, Clara, on one level or the other. Your new technology brings them into each and every living room on this planet. Overwhelming, isn't it?"

Clara only nodded. She avoided watching the news, because the violence and suffering made her feel helpless and restless. She hated feeling like that. At the same time she knew that she needed to find a way to cope with all of this other than looking away.

"You honor the spirit shield of yourself and all your fellow humans by acknowledging those wounds and calling them *sacred*," Anubis said. "It gives them the purpose they deserve, and it makes you aware that you all are on your path towards more wholeness."

He squinted. "As to the other titles you found . . . ."

He paused for some moments, but Clara did not dare to press him.

Finally he said slowly, "You know I am also called *The Jackal Headed God*. My head, they say, is one of a jackal. Is it, really? You seem to avoid looking into my face. Why, Clara? Tell me, why?"

Clara shrank back. The boat rocked bodefully. Had she heard a trace of impatience in his voice?

The thought caused her jaw to clench, and she jutted her chin as her fingers curled into fists. Almost as quickly as the anger surged, it dissipated, and the tension in her shoulders melted away. Anubis was right to ask her those questions, and he was correct; she was afraid— too afraid, even, to stare into his eyes. In spite of their intimate moments together, she allowed his face to appear as a hazy blur. She had not dared to fine-tune her focus to follow the lines of his face. She shied away, yet at the same time condemned herself for her cowardice. Silently, she hoped she could forever get away with this, but now she saw the illusion in her secret wish.

"I don't know," she mumbled, her gaze fixing on something invisible at the bottom of the boat. The water softly gurgled, and in the distance, an animal screeched ominously.

Clara had not yet been aware of any animals in this place. Why now? she wondered. Suddenly something fluttered against her face, and she screamed. In her periphery, a little bird-like creature moved away from her at an incredible speed. Its tiny wings looked like a bat's. She shuddered. Would she dare to look at his face? Would this be the moment when her dream exploded into a thousand pieces and left her stranded with nothing left but the raw feeling of being alone again?

Then he repeated his question, the tone of his voice gentler. When she still did not respond, he said quietly, "You do not feel safe with me, Clara. What can I do to make you feel safe?"

Her mind and heart raced. Then her shoulders dropped, and she sighed. "I *do* want to see you as you are," she said. "But I am full of fear. How can there be an animal face with a human voice?" When he didn't answer, she straightened up. "I guess I fear the scattering of my illusions. I—I do not want to stop myself from connecting with you."

"Have you ever heard of shapeshifting?"

She crossed her arms, uncrossed them, then crossed them again.

"Vaguely," she said.

"It also works the other way around."

"What do you mean?"

"A shaman can shapeshift into any form he or she can dream of. The reality we live in is as we dream it. If you want to change it, your dreaming power must be strong. You use your intent and your imaginative capabilities to move into another reality and create the new self. When your intent is strong enough . . . ."

"What then?" Clara asked.

"When your intent is strong enough," he continued, "your new form will be manifested in the physical world, too."

"What are you trying to tell me with all this?" Clara furrowed her brow.

"What kind of face would you wish me to show you?" he retorted.

She closed her eyes. A slight breeze blew across the water, cooling her neck and warm cheeks.

"A human face," she said quietly. "Something in me is so afraid of your inhumanness. You are said to have an animal face. You are also said to be an Egyptian god, yet you talk to me as if you are a human being. I feel close to you, and at the same time, I am shying away. Yes, it is true. I do not dare to look too close."

Moments passed before he spoke again. "How do you imagine this human face to be?"

Clara's eyes remained tightly closed.

"How can I tell?"

The moment she spoke, an image of a male face emerged behind her eyes, surfing from the darkness, then dropping away within a split second.

"See, you know!" he whispered, his voice betraying his smile. He lightly touched her left hand with his fingertips.

Clara froze. She had been unaware that he'd moved close to her.

"Come and explore my face," he murmured. "And keep your eyes closed."

He slowly took her hand and directed it towards him.

Terror rose in Clara's throat, and she fought not to cry out. *What will I touch? Does he have animal fur?*

The tips of her fingers instead brushed his skin—soft and smooth skin, human skin. Her fingers moved as if with a mind of their own, sliding slowly until she felt a a ridge beneath the skin, then a hollow. A cheekbone, then a cheek.

She became more daring. Gently her fingers retraced his face, went all the way to the ear, rested at the earlobes. She searched for his hairline, and when she found it, she slowly ran her fingers through his hair. It flowed soft and long, all the way down over his shoulders. Boldly she twisted strands of hair around two of her fingers and lightly tugged at it. Her eyes still closed, she released his hair and traced her fingers back to his face, until her palms touched his lips. They were warm and full, and when she glided along them, his breath warmed her hands. The delicate intimacy of the moment settled around her, and she realized she was smiling, thoroughly enjoying every second.

"What about opening your eyes now?"

Clara did not hesitate. His face was so near that she only saw a dark brown patch in front of her, and she jerked her head back, fighting the impulse to jump up. She closed and opened her eyes again, and there were his eyes.

Staring into hers.

"Dive into my features," he whispered.

When she moved back to see him more fully, he was smiling. His longish face held high cheekbones and a high forehead. His skin was a deep brown, and his evenly-shaped lips were a shade lighter than his skin. Her eyes wandered from his face down to his shoulders. His body was slim. His handsomeness surprised her. Though he sat, she could tell he was taller than average. He appeared peacefully calm, though his whole body seemed to shimmer with an inner light, the source of which she was not able to discover. She shook her head in bewilderment and covered her face with her hands. The sight of him so near was just too intense.

"Let us have a rest," he said softly. He turned and steered the boat back to the shore.

It was the first time he'd been the one who decided to head back.

Clara climbed out of the boat and walked lightly towards the stairs. Then she turned to wave goodbye.

There he stood at the boat's end, a black figure with a long stick in his hand. Only his silhouette remained visible to Clara, but it caused a shiver to ripple through her body.

There was no doubting what she saw.

Two long, erect ears and an equally long, narrow muzzle stood out against the darkening night sky.

* * *

Clara awoke to the sound of her own screaming.

The last scene of her dream had tossed her out of her sleep. Hundreds of jackal heads had piled up in the corner of a dark catacomb-like cellar. She could not recall how she got into that cellar and why. She had been tumbling around, searching for something she did not know. A sudden flash of light illuminated the scene, and she'd frozen at the sight of it.

Then she had heard that horrific scream.

Only when her eyes recognized the familiar features of the furniture in her room did she realize that it was she who had screamed.

She was trembling and covered in sweat. Her eyes searched the darkened corners of the room. With much effort, she raised her arms over her head and stroked them with both hands to reassure herself and her body that everything was okay.

That was intense. His voice came from her right side.

She winced, then let out a loud sigh. "Anubis," she said, relieved. Then her body tensed, and she covered her face. She was not yet ready to acknowledge him in her apartment.

"Did you chop them off?" he asked calmly.

"Did I what?" A wave of hot anger rushed through her body, eliminating her feeling of paralysis.

"Did you chop them off whenever you did not want to see the face of truth," I asked.

"I touched your face the other day! It was a human face."

"Both faces are faces of truth. It is a dead-end road to believe in images. Who knows what is true or not? Mind you, have you seen your own head in that dream?" He chuckled. "Maybe you were a she-jackal yourself?"

She stared into the dark, bewildered.

"Have you looked into a mirror during those precious occasions?"

"Of course not," she bellowed. "The idea never occurred to me."

"So maybe you want to ask for a mirror next time." He laughed. "Or what about now?"

Clara's hands flew to her face, half expecting to find it covered with fur. Her skin did not feel any different than when she went to bed.

"You never know," Anubis said inside her head. "We are all dreaming in here. And if it is a potent and good dream, you might even smell something! Wonderful fragrances, fragrances you have never smelled before! Sweet and fragile, like the first spring flowers. Or possibly . . ." he paused, "the strong animal smell of a jackal's body."

"I do not know anymore what is real and what is not real," she moaned. "Tell me!"

"Everything is real, and nothing is real," he answered. "Your imaginative power is so much stronger than you think. It creates and destroys worlds. Everything you see here is your thought forms manifested. When you chop off heads and put them in a cellar, you might have decided that you do not want to see what is there. Know that you have not really transformed the thought forms. You have simply suppressed them. They have a life of their own. There will be a time when you will be confronted with them again."

He fell silent, intuiting her need to process his words.

"That is okay," he then said. "Just know it. Everything will come to the light. Everything. In those times, all those hidden secrets will be brought into consciousness to be released and healed."

* * *

Clara gathered all her courage and went down those stairs to the lake again. When she saw Anubis standing at the shore, she sighed her relief. His features were human. His fine face with its dark eyes emanated tranquility and joy. It was daylight, and for the first time, she took a closer look at his cape. It fell in loose folds all the way down to his feet, which were covered in plain sandals. The crinkles of the cape hung perfectly still, and his hood lay on his shoulders. When she noticed his amiable look as she appraised him, she became nervous and looked away.

The boat was not there. She walked towards him and peered across the clear water. Then she shrugged. "What are we up to today?" she asked, pretending to be more bold than she felt.

"You called me," he said casually. "It is all up to you." He slowly sat down on the sandy ground. Wind ruffled the surface of the glassy water for a moment, then it eventually died down.

"But how do I know?" She propped her hands on her hips.

"There is a lot to explore, and I need to choose."

"You might not be the one to choose this time."

"What do you mean?"

"You are the one choosing and the one chosen. Chosen by whatever true impulse emerges from the inside of the holographic web of consciousness."

Clara scowled. "This sounds like hieroglyphics to me. What am I to do?"

"Calm your mind and become receptive," he said. "Out of the silence, impulses will reach out to you. You will be able to choose which one to follow from a place of centeredness and truth."

They were quiet for a while. Clara tried to concentrate on the still water. After some time, she spoke vehemently. "I am too nervous. There is nervousness, and there is boredom at the same time. My mind goes havoc. I do not feel any impulse. There might be no impulse coming. What am I then to do?" The traces of panic in her voice caused her even more anxiety.

"Stop thinking about *doing* all the time," he said calmly.

"Okay, okay," she said. "I am just a bit tense." She laughed, but it came out tight and uneasy.

"What is your fear, Clara?"

"What do I do if I do not do anything?"

He rolled his eyes. "Well try, for a change, to drop everything and just *be*."

"Just be," she echoed. "Feels like endless boring eternity when I drop into the 'just be' state."

"It is eternal," he said. "You are right."

"Oh no!" She gasped. "It feels horrible. I might be dying by just being. They might write on my gravestone, *She died while being*."

Anubis laughed. "What a sweet death," he then said.

"What do you mean by 'sweet death'? Nothing happens in this scary state of being!"

"You are afraid of the void," he said slowly.

"No!" Clara bit her lower lip. "Well, maybe a little," she reluctantly admitted.

"See, you do not even know whether you are afraid or not," he said, "because you do not even dare to go near it. The void makes people very uneasy. Especially in these times, where so much seems to be happening *out there*. Believe me, the void is a portal. There is a whole new world in the void. You should have a go!"

"But there is nothing in there!"

"You mean, no physical manifestations?" he asked, smiling. "Are you sure?"

She eyed him suspiciously. Then she straightened. "Will you go with me?"

"I am already there," he responded.

His riddles annoyed her. "What do you mean? You can't be *there* because you are *here*, here with me."

"Yes, but at the same time, I am conscious of the void inside me and that I am part of it."

"I do not understand," Clara said.

"Did you know that matter is mostly composed of space? The smallest entities your scientists discovered in human cells are called *quarks*. The space between those quarks is enormous, relative to their size. What do you think this space is made of?"

She shook her head. "I have no idea."

"Do you want to find out?" he said, his gaze resting on her face with an inexplicable expression of amusement and love.

She raised an eyebrow.

"Come on," he said. "Try it out! There are treasures to hunt. Are you not curious at all? Jump into the void, and gather experiences like squirrels their nuts." He offered another encouraging smile.

Clara reluctantly closed her eyes.

Why had she not gone to the gym with her friend Erna when she called some minutes ago? "No," she had told her. "I have an appointment. A meditation appointment, to be precise."

"Are you okay?" Erna had asked. "I mean, are you sure you do not want to go to this great spinning class?"

"I am sure," Clara had answered dryly. She remembered well the last session with Adrian, the guy who gave the course. He had made them *crawl* out of the gym hall—at least that was how her body felt after the brutal workout with him.

"You know what?" she had asked. "My meditation appointment is actually quite attractive."

There had been a pause at the other side of the telephone. Then Erna sighed. "My sweetheart, I do not want to send you to a psychotherapist, but don't you think you are a little bit too much into all this meditation business? I mean, there is life happening out here. You know this, don't you?"

"Don't worry," Clara said. "Everything is okay. I just slowed down a bit. I am actually exploring new territories."

"Will you let me know what you found out?" Erna had asked curiously.

"Yes, of course. Next time we meet!"

"Okay," Erna had said. "And I will let you know what happens with this Adrian. It looks as if this affair is ready for takeoff. I mean—you know what I mean." She paused. "We are in that stage of *catch me catch you* . . . the hide and seek game." She sighed. "Fun game, although it is a bit worn off. You know what I mean."

"Yes," Clara said. She knew indeed. You could be so hooked up to that game that you forget with whom you were playing. When you awake the next morning, you look to the phantom lying next to you, the phantom which you have created in your own imagination, and there is the dawning realization that you had just fallen again into another ego trap of illusion and projection. Then the remorse: how could I possibly . . . and all the rest.

Clara grimaced. *No, thank you.*

"You do not know this guy, Erna," she could not stop herself from saying. "Promise me to have a real close look! He just might be one of those jerks who carry a deep disrespect for the feminine, while on the outside he is covered up with sweet 'n' sticky syrup."

"Sounds like a good treat to me." Erna chuckled. "I'll be careful, I promise."

They had decided to meet the next day for breakfast and hung up.

Anubis spoke again, bringing her back to the present. "So, have you made up your mind, Clara?"

"I am just chasing off some images," she mumbled.

She took a deep breath. "My throat is itchy."

"Do you want to explore what there is to discover?" Anubis asked.

She nodded.

"Move into your throat with your awareness, and see what happens."

What does he mean, move into your throat? Another one of those mysterious riddles! At the same time, she could already see herself somehow gliding along the inside of her neck and into her throat.

And now?

"Move into one of the cells," he said.

33

There she was. Right in the center of one of those millions of cells.

Everything was quiet. After a short while, she noticed a faint buzzing. When she concentrated on it, it increased in vigor. After a while it subsided until it stayed on one level. It calmed her down. She realized she was entering a trance-like state. It was as if she'd lost the feeling of who she was—as if her boundaries had dissolved, and she *became* the low buzzing tone.

"What are you experiencing?" Anubis asked in a low voice.

"It is very peaceful here." Her words sounded dreamy. "Peaceful and energizing. I could stay like this forever."

"This is the *forever* state, in its purest form. It is when awareness penetrates space. Any guess what is in the center of awareness, Clara?"

"No idea," she said absentmindedly, still drunk with the deeply relaxed feeling.

"In the center of awareness is bliss," he said calmly. "Energy in its purest form is bliss. You are able to drink it, to drown in it, to become light in it."

He sighed. "The question is whether you are courageous enough to go so far."

"Why do you need to be courageous? It is easy!"

"Well," he said slowly. "The more you drop into the void, the more you give your own underworld creatures the space to turn up. They are your shadow, your *shew*—as is the Egyptian term for it. They love to show themselves when you go so deep. When you open up to that inner space, it is an invitation for them to announce themselves."

"Underworld creatures?" Alarm immediately moved Clara out of her throat into present awareness. "What kind of creatures?"

"You will find out for yourself," Anubis said. "They are

manifested energies which you have been building up in the subconscious of your self. They have the most unusual shapes. Wait for them! You might find them quite interesting. You might even want to start conversing with them."

Clara shuddered. "Why should I want that?" Her peaceful feeling was gone—although, oddly, the buzzing had gained strength.

"They always have important messages to convey," Anubis said. "If you understand their messages—if you make peace with them— you will reach a new level in consciousness. And then . . ."

"And then?" Clara asked.

"You will see that in the center of this awareness, those stories, once felt fully within yourself, the stories around those energies will fall away."

"What do you mean, they will fall away?"

"There will be a phase where the pure energies of those creatures can be felt. Those energies will move through your body. If you do not identify yourself with them, you will experience them just as waves of energy, nothing more. You might know that this was a wave of fear, this a wave of rage or of shame. You simply let them go through you. You release the energy of those emotions in your body and in your muscles. And you continue dropping . . ."

"Until?" Clara opened her eyes.

"I knew you would ask this." Anubis grinned. "There is no 'until.' The dropping is endless. There is no ground. Just endless dropping."

Clara shuddered again. She would never go for this. Never!

She felt a stirring within her. *No! I will not! I will not respond to this impulse. No!*

"Can you feel your resistance?" Anubis asked, as if from afar.

"Of course I can." The resistance was evident. It also seemed insurmountable.

But was it? Why the hell was she curious, then?

Honestly, Clara said to herself, you already started the exploration. You are already dropping into the void.

She grimaced. *I am already testing the ground.* Then she chuckled. Which ground?

"There is a longing in every being to evolve," Anubis said, as if he had read her thoughts. "Your drive to evolve, Clara, is your major source of energy. It gives you the strength to endure much hardship and to go through a lot of pain. It gives you wings to fly. It illuminates your own very individual path towards enlightenment." His voice belied his smile.

"You must drop into the void," he added softly. "There is no way round the void. The void is inside you. You come from the void, and you will go into the void again. You might as well explore the void now."

* * *

"How is Marco, by the way?" Erna asked, throwing two heavy books on Clara's sofabed.

"Okay, I guess." Clara picked up one of the books.

Erna looked at her uncomprehendingly.

Clara smiled uneasily. "We decided to give ourselves a bit of a rest."

Erna's mouth dropped open. "Why is that?"

"Don't look at me like that," Clara shouted. "We both needed a break. We had been quarrelling nonstop!"

"What did you quarrel about?"

Clara sighed. "The usual argument. He says I work too much,

and I won't spend enough time with him. He calls it *quality time*, and I still have not understood the concept of it!" Clara picked at her skirt. "I am tired of listening to him lament about having no success with selling his film ideas, Erna. Nobody understands him, he says. Well, maybe he is right. I do not understand him either." She wheezed. "We are pretty much stuck, Erna. We have not even made love for weeks now. You know, that had always been one of the areas which worked, somehow. I just became tired of the usual 'hype me up' style approach."

Clara's brows knit. "I must confess . . . it was me breaking the rules," she murmured. "So now, he is even more angry." She stared out of the window. "Let's change the subject; otherwise, I will get too frustrated. What are these books about?"

Erna smiled mischievously. "Yeah," she said, suddenly glowing. "I found something for you. Two books on power animals to get you more acquainted with the jackal world." Her smile deepened, but a trait of jealousy colored her voice. Only a few days ago, she had said to Clara with a comical sigh, "I wish he would speak to *me*! I guess only the chosen ones are the ones entering heaven, so please, please put in a good word for me when you pass those portals, will you? I do not want to turn sour in the hell of ignorance."

Clara moaned. Then she pulled herself together again.

"Great idea," she said, not knowing herself how much irony she wanted to load into those words. She went over to Erna to hug her.

How lucky am I to have such a friend, she thought. Who else could I talk to about *just anything* in my life, about my stagnant relationship with Marco as well as those incredible and seemingly ludicrous encounters with this strange being from the other world?

She is like an anchor to me, Clara pondered while enjoying Erna's smooth cheek on her face.

Without her, I might go insane. She grimaced. *But with her, I might still go insane!*

Clara laughed. "Want a goddess rinse?"

Erna jumped back. "A goddess what? Good grief, what is this supposed to be?"

"It is a real treat for the she-humans of this world. I had the pleasure to get to know it recently in a workshop." Clara smiled. "Let me show you."

She went to her CD player and put in her favorite CD. Kirtana's soft, feminine voice started meandering through the room. The last rays of the sun were just disappearing behind the buildings on the other side of the street. Dusk was about to settle in, infusing the room with a dark blue that gathered at the corners and then spread out from there. The twilight provided just enough light for the two women to see each other's silhouettes.

Clara lit some candles on the table and returned to Erna.

"Close your eyes," she said quietly. She then raised her arms above her head and gently laid them on Erna's head. Slowly she stroked down Erna's hair, letting the silken-blonde strands glide through her fingers. Then she followed the line of Erna's neck with her hands, moved over to the shoulders, and gradually all the way down Erna's arms to the tips of her fingers. Now Clara had her eyes closed, too.

The atmosphere in the room shifted. There was an inexplicable intensity and softness building up. The sweet scent of the candles merged with the more pungent incense Clara had burned before Erna had arrived. Clara asked Erna to breathe slowly and steadily. She noticed her own breath following Erna's rhythm and becoming indistinguishable from hers. It was as if the ebb and flow of their in-and-out breaths were the only thing in the world.

Surrender to your own movements, Clara thought—or was it Anubis whispering those words into her ears? She felt as if she'd dropped deeper into her body while she moved her hands along the sides of Erna's body. Her movements did not seem to be *her* movements anymore. A powerful and calming force within her had taken over, making her hands move like semifluid liquid, not unlike lava slowly blazing its trail into untouched territory.

Erna let out a long sigh. Her head dropped backwards.

"This is so good," she mumbled.

Clara's hands were slowly moving down from Erna's shoulders through the middle line of her chest and across her solar plexus. There they rested some moments before they moved further down, out to her hips and then all the way down the legs to her feet.

When Clara completed her gentle strokes, Erna moaned.

"What is heaven compared to this?" she whispered and let out a long, bliss-filled breath. "This *is* heaven. No need to wait in front of any portals to be let in. Thank you so much, Clara. I feel very calm now."

"I knew you would enjoy it." Clara grinned up from where she now kneeled on the floor in front of her friend. "A goddess rinse!" She laughed lightly, stood, and let herself fall onto the sofa.

Erna opened her eyes and slowly focused on Clara with the air of having come from a faraway place. Her eyes were like deep pools of dark water.

The two friends gazed into each other's eyes in wordless understanding. Then Clara nodded as if to confirm an unspoken truth.

She grabbed one of the books and opened it. "Jackal, jackal," she muttered. "Where is the chapter on jackal?" When she found it, she started to read.

* * *

Forget about those books. Anubis's voice held a stern tone. She looked up and had the flickering sensation of a shadow emerging from the corner.

"You won´t find your answers in those books. Ask me. You will get clearer answers, I promise."

"Sorry," Clara said evasively and put the books aside.

"What are you saying?" Erna shouted from the kitchen, where she had gone to prepare some food.

"I am not talking to you," Clara shouted back to Erna. This is getting increasingly schizophrenic, she thought grimly. She put the book aside, stood up, and went over to Erna.

"Let me help you with the salad," she said, opening the fridge. "Do you want lemon or balsamico for the dressing?"

Erna pushed her aside and shoved her out of the kitchen.

"It is my turn," she said impatiently. "You go back to studying those books."

Clara sighed. Not much of a chance here, she thought.

She dropped back down on the sofa. "I am going to switch on the telly. Just to distract myself from all this stuff," she murmured.

"Why are you withdrawing?" Anubis asked. "Can you tell me what is up, Clara?"

She stared into the air. For heaven's sake! "I just don't want them to be scavengers!" she then blurted out, much to her surprise.

"What do you have against scavengers?"

Clara did not answer. Her mind told her that it was ridiculous to feel disgusted, yet she could not help it. Images of jackals rummaging with their noses in dead animal corpses kept turning up in her head. She covered her nose against the sensation of a putrid stench. Horrible, she thought, shivering.

Why did he need to have a jackal face?

"Clara, there is nothing abominable in this world. Nothing. This world is made of the six sacred elements dancing their sacred dance."

"Six!" she said, disconcerted. "I always thought there are only five!"

"There are six," he said calmly. "You know them all: it is wood, fire, earth, metal, water—and actually, the void, which you so fancy to explore. Since millions of years, those six elements have danced the dance of forms. They transform into each other, they merge with one another, they build a myriad of another million compositions each moment anew. 'To dust you will return.' This is the saying of one of your major religions. Well, before you turn into dust, you might as well become a feast for another living creature, don't you think?"

He seemed amused by her resentment.

Clara did not utter a word.

She heard him sighing. "Has it ever occurred to you," he then said in a soothing tone, "that animals are as divine as human beings? Have you ever consciously looked into the eyes of an animal and made contact with its pure essence, its soul? You would notice that animals do not hide anything. They are not able to hide anything. Their beingness is transmitted through their eyes, purely, innocently. If you have an image of this animal in your head, you will shrink back, because you will project your image upon the animal the moment you look into its eyes."

Anubis paused for a moment, then said, "The Egyptians knew about the sacredness of animals. They deeply appreciated their individual essence. They saw their physical appearances as a sacred vessel for very specific and indeed unique divine vibrations."

He laughed merrily.

"They were great shamans; they knew how to merge their vibrations with the animals to experience them from the core of their beings, or from the depths of their cells. They knew what those specific vibration feels like and how powerful they are. All shamans of this world strive to become masters in vibrations. This is how they gain access to amazing powers outside the human realm. They let themselves be taught by the animal world."

Clara shivered.

"What does a jackal stand for?" she then asked.

"You need to find out yourself. I wouldn't ever want to take that experience away from you," Anubis said. "Look into a jackals's eyes and meditate with it. You will feel its essence quickly."

Although Clara could not see him, she suddenly had the impression that he was looking at her with great intent.

"Is this an invitation?"

"Well, why not? You might as well do it now."

Her look fell into one of the darker corners in her living room. Was he emerging from the dark? Were her eyes still open? She did not know. Suddenly she had the sensation of her gaze being magnetized to a pair of brown eyes. A fresh smell, sappy and full of impetuousness and life power, reached her nose. It was the scent of blood. She sniffed deeply. The pure joy of being alive filled her. It was a playful liveliness, playful and boisterous.

Clara laughed out loud. Life is fun, flickered through her mind. "Why make things complicated when it really is so easy." She laughed again.

Then it rushed into her. Even the tiger, when he is about to jump onto you, is not filled with evil, she thought. Rather, he is completely balanced in the now, with nothing evil in his mind. He is just doing what his instincts are playing out. "Go, get some food," those instincts tell him ferociously.

"Right you are," Anubis said. "Do not project evil onto any animal. It is pure life force that makes the jackal tear away those pieces of meat. There is sacredness in there. Imagine being a jackal. Feel how your muscles contract and expand, how they relax, how he is all attentive while the rest of his body is in a complete state of relaxation. There is not one muscle which is unnecessarily tense. He is utterly present and alive."

Again, laughter bubbled from Clara's mouth. She felt powerful and vitalized.

Then her stomach growled.

I am hungry, she realized with surprise. I want to eat meat, red meat.

Her hunger grew stronger, and she imagined herself jumping to her feet and running, following the smell of meat, the smell of another animal which had just lost its last fight to a mightier enemy. From afar, she heard dogs howling. She sniffed the air. "Where is the smell coming from?" she murmured. "Where are you?"

Erna's voice brought her back to the present. Startled, she turned around and saw her friend appear from the kitchen, waving some printouts in her hands. Without looking at Clara, Erna read from a pamphlet in a loud and theatrical voice, "In the Egyptian necropolis, the wild dogs of ancient times would often prowl to hunt for food. There is a legend that Anubis took the form of a jackal to help Isis and Nephthys search for the pieces of Osiris' body."

Erna stopped reading. "Isn't this interesting?" she exclaimed. "Listen to this! Anubis was also called *He Who is in the Place of Embalming*. In the funerary rites, a priest wore the mask of Anubis to assist in the so-called 'Opening of the Mouth Ceremony'."

Finally, Erna glanced at Clara. "Oh my goddess! What is the matter with you?"

Clara tried to speak, but only a barking sound left her mouth.

Erna rushed towards her and shook her violently.

"Clara, can you please get yourself together. You look like an animal going berserk."

"Did you say . . . those priests were . . . wearing masks?" Clara asked.

"Yes, this is what I said, but for heaven's sake, why does this shock you so much?"

Clara's voice cracked as she spoke. "Even the tiger, when he is about to jump onto you, is not filled with evil."

"What are you talking about?" Erna cried.

Clara frowned. "How far did you get with our meal? I thought you wanted to cook. I am starving."

Erna's eyes were wide as her mouth dropped open. "I *am* cooking," she protested. "But I am a multitasker, as you might know. And guess what, my dear one? I was getting pretty tired of all this raw food stuff we have eaten in the last weeks. I bought us a gigantic T-bone steak, which I have just thrown into the pan. No objections allowed from your side! Tonight we are going to have heaps of meat!"

Erna's eyes sparkled with joy when she turned towards the kitchen. Clara felt her face changing into a contorted grimace. Well done, she thought. I have no idea how this came about, but I am for sure grateful for this telepathic exchange of information here.

* * *

"I am losing it again," she said in a hushed voice.

"Yes, my love, I can see it," he responded calmly while moving the stick slowly through the waters.

The sun was disappearing, and darkness encroached upon them. The few trees near the lake's shore threw gigantic and strangely crooked shadows onto its surface. The shadows moved in the slight breeze. Like ethereal beings dancing to inaudible music, living a haunting life of their own, Clara thought.

"You are in quite a turmoil. What happened?" Anubis asked.

"I just saw this angel," Clara said with a repressed voice.

Anubis smiled. "Oh, really?" An amused smile played across his lips. "Have your eyes finally adjusted to their frequency? How did the angel look?"

"I only saw those wings with tips in shades of blue and violet. There were also rags of orange and yellow." Clara hesitated. "Mostly, it was pure white light, shiny and glistening. I also received a message." She hid her face behind her hands.

"Sooo?" Anubis asked.

"Well, the message was that it was me. Me! How presumptuous! I am so ashamed of even telling *you*." Clara fell silent, and when she finally spoke, it took great effort. "Well, it was a nice vision."

"It was a *nice vision?* Just a *nice vision?*" Anubis raised his eyebrows. There was a mildly curious expression on his face.

"Well, yes." Clara laughed shyly. "I was flattered at first, but then I pushed it away, thinking, *Hallo! Me, an angel?* Come on, Clara, get real. But I could feel the calling from it. From him. From her. Ehh, no idea from whom." Clara shook her head. "But there was certainly a strong calling and an equally strong promise for—I do not particularly want to call it *remuneration*, but that was how it felt. Like the promise of goodies. You get goodies when you believe in the big vision." She giggled hysterically, then she frowned and became quiet again.

"How do you feel now?" he asked.

"I feel displaced. Confused. And there is a question in me, a question asking if I would be courageous enough to connect again with this angel presence, knowing this is what my heart asks for, or . . . ."

"Or what?" he asked.

When she realized he was taking her seriously, Clara relaxed. She sat upright, and when she spoke again, her voice was more confident.

"Or would I opt for identifying myself with my normal self, the one looking for security, the one wondering where and how to invest my little amount of money to save it for my rent . . . and so on and so forth."

She sighed.

"I feel as if I am often asked to take a big step, but no one tells me if I would be stepping right into the abyss. I probably am. I also wonder whether stepping into the abyss might not be more comfortable than forcing myself to stay away from it. In fact, it might not only be more comfortable but possibly also—some sort of ecstatic. Huh? It might be—ecstatic?" She rolled her eyes theatrically.

"Yep," he said gloomily. "You never know what is waiting there in the abyss. Hell or Heaven. A big monster or a great lover. You never know." He smiled, and a mischievous glint lit his eyes. Then he chuckled, slapping his hands on his legs. "Besides, you do not even know which is better."

"Come on, Anubis! Do not pretend to be the cool guy. You are pretty aware of the fact that I am a bit—afraid. Off center. Off the hook, so to say."

"Absolutely." His grin grew broader. "What about hooking into the angel presence again?"

Clara gasped. "Are you joking?"

"Not really." He turned serious again. "What are you afraid of?"

"Don't know," she murmured. "I guess it is this image I have of angels. It makes me choke. They seem so pure. Only good. Only holy. No mistakes, no failures, just perfectly holy. It is a high standard they set."

"You do not like to be holy?" Anubis struggled not to smile.

"Oh no," she answered impulsively. She hung her head. "I guess I should. I mean, should we not all try to be as good as possible?" Clara cleared her throat.

"For sure." Anubis nodded. "Trying to be good is probably the most efficient way to make your demons move. Once they make themselves known, I encourage you to suppress them with great force." He smiled ironically.

She rubbed her arms. "Don't play games with me."

"Well, as a matter of fact, this was done for centuries. Suppress the demons? You were just giving them more energy food with that. And then you humans were all surprised when they came up to the surface, soaring into your face, howling like mad."

"So, where are the hidden monsters of the angels then?" Clara asked provocatively.

"White contains all colors." Anubis turned his face towards her. "Believe me, if a monster shows up in the face of an angelic being, it is immediately transformed by the angel's pure presence and compassion. Angels accept the fact that nothing is so bad that it needs to be hidden away." He paused and watched her eyes. "It is the hiding that distorts everything."

Clara was dumbfounded. "How does the angel transform the monsters?"

"Through their capacity to *feel*. One of the most transformative feelings is self-love. If you have self-love, you will be compassionate with anything and anybody on this planet. Angels are the most compassionate beings. They are the living demonstration of how to transform all negative patterns with pure presence and love—your masculine and feminine powers."

"But they are not human! They are divine!"

"There is not one single being on this planet earth who is not divine. You'd better get used to the idea that there is an angel somewhere hiding in the depths of your being. Find it, Clara. And then enjoy!"

* * *

"He was an abandoned child," Erna said, looking up from the heavy history book she had placed on the dining table. "He was left alone in the desert by his mother. No food, no milk, no nurturing physical contact, just the empty sky above and the hot white sand beneath. He might have screamed for hours. It must have been a traumatic experience!"

"Well, he was only a baby." Clara flipped the page of an antique book on Egyptian artwork. She admired an ancient stone carving of the head of an Egyptian high priest that reminded her of her strange experience at the museum.

"He couldn't possibly remember this," she added.

Erna gave her a look of disbelief. "What do you mean?" She waved in agitation. "Everybody knows everything. It is just a question when it rises up into your consciousness, that's all!"

Clara glanced up. "Pardon me? I do not understand."

Erna stared at her, her eyes turning dark. A shadow of sadness flickered over her face. "I was with a bodyworker yesterday," she said slowly. "She asked me to lie on her massage table. Then she held various points at the back of my body. When she was at the level of my heart, I felt intense pain. I nearly screamed! She did not want me to go further into my emotions. She simply asked whether I had any thoughts or images about this pain. I suddenly felt myself floating in my mother's womb. It was warm and dark there . . . ."

Erna's voice broke. After a moment, she pulled herself together again and continued with much effort. "The feeling of loneliness was overwhelming, Clara. She was not with me. She was with my brother Karl, who had been born three years before me and who had seriously fallen ill. The doctors had told her that he would be dying soon. Her agonizing soul stayed with him all the time. She was not with me, the other child growing in her womb. I was being taken care of physically, but emotionally, I could only feel the disconnection, the void, the emptiness. There was no one. There was no one tuning into me, whispering to me in a soft murmuring voice, telling me how much I was welcome here. She did not dare to welcome me. Her pain was so big that she was afraid she would die if she built up a strong connection to me."

Tears streamed down Erna's face, but she continued to look into Clara's eyes as if they anchored her at the surface, preventing her from drowning in a sea of sadness.

"I felt so abandoned. Many years later, when I looked at photos from that time, I realized how this experience with my brother changed my mother. She was so radiant with my older three brothers. When I was born, and Karl died two years later, her eyes were broken. They never regained that radiance, I was told. Those were my first years on this planet. They were deeply imprinted by her pain about the loss of my elder brother."

Clara's hands trembled. "Oh my goodness. I did not know this." She softly touched Erna's shoulder, then she embraced her silently.

"I am with you," she then murmured into Erna's ear. "Can you feel me? Can you feel my arms around your body, holding you tight, the skin of my face touching yours? Can you feel me, Erna?"

Erna slowly nodded, and her shoulders sagged. Her body lost its rigidity and became soft. She sighed deeply.

"It is good that you are here," she whispered. "Thank you so much, Clara."

Erna placed a hand to her chest, her head leaning against Clara's body. "I can feel something growing together within myself—as if two halves are trying to become whole again. It is good to have shared this story with you. Thank you!"

Clara hugged her friend again. The two stood together in the dark room until the church bell rang nine times.

"It is late," Erna said. "Would you be okay if I stayed with you? I do not want to be on my own tonight."

"Sure!" Clara smiled. "I'd love you to be my guest. Let's make beds and go to sleep. It's been an intense day."

* * *

Clara woke up in the middle of the night. She lay still a moment, listening to Erna's rhythmic breathing. Then she again heard the sound that had woken her, the howling outside. It was the howling of an approaching storm, rare in the area in which she lived. The storm had been announced on television, and people were advised to stay inside.

She listened to the storm with increasing alertness. It was picking up in strength. Leaves and small twigs from the old poplars outside her apartment pinged against her bedroom windows. Wind violently tossed the street lanterns backwards and forwards, casting wildly moving shadows onto her living-room walls. Clara shivered. Her mind wandered back to the conversation she'd had with Erna. *For fuck's sake, why?* She switched on her reading light and took a pen and paper. With big letters, she wrote *WHY?* on top of the page. Then she crossed out the words several times, pressing down hard with the pen. She would never get a response which would ring true to her. Never!

Yes, she knew of all those spiritual theories on karma, debts, lessons to be learnt, and contracts concluded before the individual soul's incarnation. She would, however, never understand and accept that children were taken from their mothers, abandoned, left alone. She would never accept an elaborate explanation for her mother's early death, her crossing over to the other side of the veil, as they so poetically said, when she was just seven years old. It was cruel; this was all it was. Life was simply cruel.

She threw aside her duvet, got up, and went into the kitchen. Carefully, she closed the kitchen door behind her in order to not disturb Erna. Then she switched on the light and sat down. She noticed that she had been clenching her fist. It hurt. Slowly and with much effort, she opened them again. Rage, anger, and helplessness surged through her in chaotic, oscillating currents. There was a burning sensation around her heart, and tension built within her, tormenting her, mirroring the storm outside. The growling and swirling seemed as much inside her body as outside her home, and her heart felt like it was becoming a dark and constricting black hole.

Then she heard a familiar voice.

"Watch out that you are not being sucked into this vortex," Anubis said calmly. "You would not want that, really. It might be difficult to find your way back into your heart."

"Where are you?" she asked, bewildered.

"You are tormenting yourself with your thoughts, Clara, and you are confused. You think it is something out there you need to fight against. There is nothing out there. It is all within you. When you fight out there, you are actually fighting in here."

With those words, a sudden stabbing pain pierced her heart.

"In here. Do you hear me, Clara?"

An explosion of pain burst in her chest. Clara heard someone screaming. Horrified, she saw red and yellow flames blazing out of her chest. She beat at them with her hands, yet they grew stronger.

Hands reached out to her, but she did not know whose hands they were. The hands pushed at her shoulders, and she screamed as she whirled around and fell into the fire. Flames shot upward and engulfed her body. The heat was excruciating. At the same time, Clara experienced herself somehow outside the fire, watching herself from above, a witness observing her own burning. She panicked, yet at the same time she also felt peculiarly detached from the scene, as if she was moving backwards and forwards from the one panicking and the one witnessing: horrified one second and detached the next while watching the complete and utter burning of the body.

The body turned into an indefinable mass of black volcanic material, then it melted away. Images of herself as a child appeared in the smoke. She saw how lonely she had been and how her built-up anger fueled her protests about this unjust world. How very much she suffered in her isolation and abandonment! The flames licked at the remaining parts of what she perceived as her body until they gave up. Slowly, the flames died out. There was nothing left—no will, no rage, no pain. Nothing. Everything was gone. Even the noise of the storm had ebbed away. Silence penetrated everything.

"How do you feel now?" The comfortingly familiar voice came from inside, from a place which did not exist anymore, and yet she seemed to be the source of this voice.

"Incredibly light," she answered after a while, sounding ephemeral. "I just feel incredibly light. I feel light as a feather."

He laughed quietly. "You passed a test here. Your heart is as light as a feather. You allowed it to be burnt completely. If I were to weigh it against the feather of Ma'at at the end of your days, you might actually be allowed into the Egyptian heavens."

Clara stared at him, his voice still echoing in her body.

"Whenever you feel pain in your heart, call the sacred fire and move into it. Be willing to let the pain come up, then let it go. Do not care about anything other than just the fire. Ignore all those mental explanations. Let the fire extinguish your burdens. Be the sacred witness for the pain you let go. The fire is sacred, as are all the other elements from which the earth is made. Welcome the fire, and ask it to burn away your pain."

Silence surrounded her for a while, then she heard him saying, as if from afar, "know that I am with you always. I am the one guiding the initiates through their underworlds. They are all asked to face and transform their most sacred wounds. I bring them to stand face to face with Ma'at so that she can do her work. Now you know why I am called *The Weigher of Hearts in the Halls of Amenti*. Do not burden your heart with worries, or anger, or shame, or guilt. When you notice a burden, set your intent to transform it and go into the fire."

When Clara opened her eyes, Erna stood at the kitchen door, rubbing her eyes. "What are you doing here?" she asked sleepily. "Come back to bed. It is cold in there without you."

* * *

"Okay, here we go." Erna waved a piece of paper in her right hand. "I have printed it out. The list."

"What list?" Clara yawned. She had just come home from another crazy day at her office. One of her most important clients had complained about the latest design layouts. Her boss had been all over the place, with red spots on her cheeks and a screechy voice, ransacking through papers and casting menacing looks at everybody.

Clara sighed. Sometimes I doubt the importance of my work, she thought ironically. But she was glad that this time she was not in the front line, face to face with those disgruntled clients.

Just one of those days when we were all on the rack again, she contemplated, torn between clients' expectations, the requirement to work efficiently (each minute was taken note of to be passed on to the clients on the monthly bill), and the demand to stay polite no matter how impertinent the clients were. And then, all these long hours of work! Some colleagues had recently quit their jobs. She missed them.

"Come on, Clara. I told you I would look up *sacred wounds*," Erna said.

"Oh." Clara turned to her. "Did you find anything?"

"Well, at first I did not find much, but then I decided to use another word for *sacred wound*." Again, Erna waved her sheet of paper. "I searched for the word *trauma*, and guess what? Millions of hits. Do you think I could use *trauma* instead of *wound*?"

"Yep," Clara nodded. "I bet Anubis would agree."

"I found a list which makes it quite clear." Erna started rattling down the first points. Then she sat down. "I need to slow down," she said. "This is serious stuff. I am sorry, Clara."

Clara jerked back. Her heart had contracted when Erna had started reading the first point. She'd learned by now that she needed to take her body's signals seriously.

Respect, she thought and breathed in deeply. I am owing myself respect. Respect to my story, and respect to everyone else's story here on this planet.

"According to Anubis, we all came here to this earth to learn and make our experiences," Clara said quietly. "I am not sure whether we really know what is waiting here for us."

Clara bent forward to the list and began to read.

- *Early traumata*

- *Birth*

- *Near death drowning*

       (=Global high activation)

- *Rape*

- *Violence*

- *Assaults*

       (=Unavoidable attacks)

- *Operations*

- *Anesthesia*

- *Burns*

       (=Physical injuries)

- *Accidents*

- *Falls*

- *Head injuries*

       (=High-impact experiences)

- *Losses of beloved ones*

- *Abandonment*

- *Betrayal*

    (=Emotional traumas)

- *Earthquakes*

- *Floods*

- *Fire*

- *Social changes*

    (=Nature disasters)

- *Torture*

- *Ritual abuse*

- *Concentration camps*

    (=Horror)

- *Third Reich*

- *Slavery*

- *Genocide*

    (=Collective traumatas)

Slowly Clara put down the list. She felt crestfallen.

Erna watched Clara's face, then spoke hesitantly. "There might be more. You know . . . someone told me recently about past-life experiences. Believe it or not, you might also carry unresolved past-life experiences into your present life."

"Oh my goddess," Clara murmured. "For each of those experiences on this list, I would probably be able to come up with the names of one or more people I know."

Her hands trembled. She tried to stop it, but to no avail. Her body seemed to have a mind of its own. With much willpower, she stood and motioned Erna to follow her. "Let us go out into the *Englischer Garten*," she said wretchedly. "I have that feeling of drowning into an abyss. It is time to sit on a patch of green grass and watch the leaves fluttering in the wind!"

Without a word, Erna put on her jacket.

"I have no idea what we are going to do with all of this, Erna," Clara said when she stepped out of the house and into the blazing sun. I have no idea where all this research leads us to. I have the feeling, though, that there is someone or something guiding us here."

With a loud bang, the door fell back into its place.

3

HER STORY

The following day, Clara wrote in her diary.

I am a woman from Germany. I am a German woman. I am German. My father was born in 1932. He was seven years old when World War II began. My mother was born in 1940, in the first half of the second world war, when Hitler was at his peak of success in succumbing all neighbor states into slavery.

They have classified me anew. I am called a child of the war-children's generation. This is the new term which has risen up in the current German debate; The "Children of the War Children." "Die Kinder der Kriegskinder."

I am no child anymore. I am a young German woman with a typical German history, I assume.

My father's father had felt the catastrophe breaking Germany down. When Hitler took power in 1933, he was quoted saying, "This is a black day in the history of the Germans." I never met him. He died early. He was a baker, originally, but during the war, he was a day-laborer. He was a simple man with a wise heart.

My mother's grandfather was a true vassal of Hitler. He was educated. He even went abroad in his early twenties to study modern methods of agriculture. There is a photo of him standing besides the channel of Panama. As he was an expert in agriculture, Hitler sent him to Poland to organize the settlement of the "pure Aryan race." First, the Polish people needed to be dislodged from their farms: mothers, fathers, grandparents, children, grandchildren.

He was said to be diligent. He believed in the Führer, *and he certainly did a good job. With my grandmother, he* made *children for the* Führer. *My grandmother was pregnant at least seven times. Six of her children survived the war, one of them my beloved mother.*

Shortly before the end of the war, my grandmother received a phone call from her cousin, a high-ranking official in the SS. "Get out of that town," he yelled at her. "Take your children and get out of that town. The Russians are coming."

My grandmother was twenty-eight years old. She had six children by then. The youngest was three months old. Had she had any idea how dangerous the situation had grown?

I doubt it. She had probably been absorbed by her domestic duties. She had been brainwashed all those years with news about a glorious victory being close, along with those other stories, those horrendous stories about the Russians. Propaganda, lies, half-truths, truths. Who was she to know? But then, her husband must have known. Where was he when she left the house and fled? Where was my grandfather?

My grandmother had cherished the Führer, *as did many other women. They had agreed to their husbands and sons being sent to the frontline and being killed. In those last weeks of the war, when this SS man who was my great granduncle called, most women were alone with their children. They had been abandoned by their husbands, who were struggling for their lives far away from their families—if they had not yet found their final peace. Women had to learn that there was no one to protect them and their upbringings.*

My grandmother grabbed her six children, as many hands as she could hold (What about the other hands? Who held them?), took whatever she could take and whatever her older children could carry (the oldest one having just turned eight), and went to the nearby station to get the next train out. Two Polish nannies were with her, but not for long. They deserted on this flight to the West in an unnoticed moment of time. The first one had already disappeared at the station.

My granny waited for eight hours. She and her six children. Finally, a train arrived, the last train from the East. It brought her and her family into the West, into burning cities, famine, rape, and death. After a week's odyssey, she finally found safety at her husband's parents' home. She was not welcomed warmly there. They were apparently not too enthusiastic about their daughter-in-law turning up with all those children to feed.

I stood there on the platform of this small Polish town some years ago, together with Erna. We tried to fathom what she must have felt there with her six children. We could not. It was too horrifying to imagine her fear. We were afraid of being overwhelmed. Somehow, we did not entirely open our hearts. We stayed at a safe emotional distance, as if we had drawn a veil between her and us, a veil that was meant to protect our hearts.

My grandmother had never said a word about what she witnessed in those days of death and destruction. Neither did any of her children. Nobody spoke about it, and I was too young to ask my mother before she died. Much later, I saw those photos, those horrendous photos. Dead bodies rotting away on the streets, traumatized people with empty eyes straying around amidst the debris, piles of human bones and skeletons.

When the war ended, silence creeped into my family, as into most German families. This grave-like silence was meant to suppress all those monstrous emotions of shame, guilt, and fear. The silence kept all those horrendous experiences undercover. They were like twisted, gnarled, rotten roots pushed far deep into the earth.

The psychological consequences on those war children were severe. Only gradually do we, the descendants, begin to understand *the scope of them. Anxiety, panic attacks, and claustrophobia— what are the roots of these emotions?*

My uncle suffered from agoraphobia. He could not cross public squares without panicking. Was this caused by the dropping of bombs from a menacing sky? His brother had hid in the cellar when bombs crashed into his house. He did not know whether he would ever come to the surface again. Much later, he developed strange psychosomatic symptoms in his legs. They felt weak—so weak that they could not carry him any longer. Was that because all they had wanted to do, once, in an extreme moment of time, was run, run, run, and yet they were not allowed to? Had their natural instinctual response been suppressed down there in that dark cellar? Run, run, run. Those legs had been forbidden to run.

Religion was no refuge after the war.

Religion had been sneered at during the Nazi time. Why should we expect solace and even redemption from a merciful God? Where was God in all those infernos, anyway? How could He allow us to be so cruel and inhuman to the Jewish people? Why didn't He destroy us to save those people? In the face of the suffering of our victims, we had no right to acknowledge our own suffering. All those children bombed. All those women raped. All those soldiers killed. All those stories untold, all those emotions unfelt. They rumble in the underworld of my ancestors, and they still do so in my life. They rumble through all lifetimes of all generations, until they are brought to the light, acknowledged, and healed. That is what Anubis says, and I believe him.

He also says you do not need to know the story for it to be healed. It would suffice to connect with the pain of the ones within us. When we open our hearts, we initiate the healing shift.

My grandfather remained silent like a stone when his children (my mother, too, I was told), assailed him with questions, questions following presentations of photo and film material at school, reports in newspapers. How could this have happened? What have you known? What was your role in this? Your responsibility? Did you carry responsibility?

No response.

His complete shutting down of communication, his retreat into his own hell, left everybody helpless and then, at the end, mute. There was a wall of muteness around my grandfather, and nobody could break this wall. He became unreachable. And we will never know where those Polish people he had dislodged from their homes ended up. The reality might be harsher than any of the horrors we saw as endless streams of images in our minds. A creative mind can be a curse.

Clara put down her pen. What had driven her to write these things? Why had she felt an impulse to capture those memories with written words? She had felt an urge to describe the stage on which her life had unfolded. She knew intuitively that whatever had happened in those years was part of her story, too. One could even say that the cornerstones of her life were set up many years before she was born. They had carved the scene into which she had slipped, right from her mother's womb.

She remembered Erna saying back then at that station in her mother's city that this was the bedrock of Clara's life along with the constellation of those blinking night stars with their coded messages at the moment of her birth. And then, Erna had added with a smile, already a moment later, the big wheel of fate had tilted a little further, and another moment raised itself out of the void.

How can I live with such a heritage? Clara closed her eyes against the tears forming there. *And how does Anubis come into all of this?*

* * *

"They had no idea how to untie that knot," Anubis said. "They knew in their hearts that they needed to untie the giant knot weaved by their witnessing the pain of their victims, their own shame as perpetrators, the immeasurable suffering. They had no idea how to unstrap their hearts. There was no space where they felt safe enough to do so. They did not know that the only safe space is in the heart. So they became mute."

He watched Clara's face as she absorbed his words. "Then they wanted everybody else to turn mute, as well. That is why they forbade you to ask questions."

"Me?" Clara asked, her eyes growing wide.

"You don't realize how few questions you ask. You learnt their lesson well. They did not make you want to ask questions. Questions would tear at those straps around their heart and stir up those muttering monsters."

"Monsters?"

Anubis nodded. "You could call those suppressed energies *demons* or *monsters*. They are in your collective shadow. They warn you: beware! It is dangerous to ask good questions. You might wake us up. You might stir up a lot of energy. You could be overwhelmed by images and emotions."

Clara put a hand to her mouth and blinked.

"You might not even know whom those monsters belong to— whether they are yours or the person's opposite you. It does not matter."

"It does not matter?" Clara asked incredulously.

"It does not matter whose monsters they are. The energy of those monsters are moving through you and through the other person. It is a moving field of information. It contains precise messages. One message is: Don't you dare to ask! It is far too dangerous."

"But why?"

Anubis appeared reflective for a moment, obviously considering his next words. "You are living in a holographic universe. People asked your grandfather, what happened? Have you done any harm to other people? Immediately, a movie with a hundred violent images might have been rampaging in his head, images carrying shame, guilt, denial, and fear. Unknowingly, you as the inquirer had tipped the sleeping beast at its shoulders, and it roared up. You noticed immediately, although you might not have had any image of it. Your body will report to you, in less than split seconds, that you are in extreme danger. It does not matter whether those situations were from the past or not. Time does not make a difference. Your body feels the sensations of danger right now. It reacts to this particular field of information. You might be in the most protected circumstances. It does not matter."

Clara studied her hands as if they could help her understand all this.

"Why do people feel *angst* when they are in a safe environment?" Anubis asked. "There is this saying, 'FEAR is False Evidence Appearing Real.' But what is real? The whole subject of fear is centered around this phenomenon of the field of information. You know *fear* quite well, Clara, don't you?"

Clara only nodded. Her heartbeat raced. This troublesome conversation unnerved her. "Am I completely at the mercy of those situations?" she asked meekly.

"Currently, there are strong fields of fear in your world. It is good to know that those fields of information are moving through you. You are in the field, but you do not need to identify with it. This is the hardest part. You must connect with a deeper part in you through your sacred witness."

Anubis paused for a moment, then he stood and moved his hands and arms very slowly, as if they were stroking invisible strands of fibers in the air. He looked awesome in his slow motion modus. Clara knew he was very much aware of each of his movements, but he was at the same time also strangely detached from them, as if he were listening intensively to music playing far away. His trance dance mystified her, and her heartbeat calmed.

Then he stopped moving and looked at Clara. "You consciously connect with a field of love and safety. You deliberately remember a memory of a situation when you felt safe, like when your mother held you in her arms. Or when your man was fully present and loving with you. You might be pendulating for a moment between those two very different fields, between love and fear. Then you will drop into your center, like an antique clock's pendulum coming to a halt."

His voice became more urgent. "Don't try to ignore the menacing field! Your subconscious will know that you are trying to suppress something. It will be on alert. Most people are on alert all the time. They are immensely stressed."

Anubis stared off for a moment, then returned his gaze to Clara. "Stay in your sacred witness and hold the space so that the field can move and change. These are unique possibilities to grow and transform individual and collective shadows. I am called a *way-shower*. I am showing you how to face and transform your shadow, Clara, so that you can move on and find joy in your heart. This is why you called me. Many humans will call me at some stage on the path, because they want to untie those straps around the heart. I might be called differently in other traditions or lifetimes. We all serve the same purpose—to hold up the vibration of freedom and lightheartedness in a world such as yours, a world in utter pain."

* * *

"No, my grandfather never regretted it," Clara said to Erna the other day. "He never understood what he had done. Or maybe he understood his side of the story, but he did not allow the other people's pain to ever enter his heart. Who am I to know? Who am I to judge?"

"So how did he die?" Erna had asked.

Clara turned away and stared towards the sky, where darkening clouds moved in.

He died when I was six years old. I saw him tumbling down the steep garden slope behind his house. We were there, the three of us, my mother, my sister, and I, carrying baskets to pick up mirabelles from the overburdened trees. I was the closest to him, just about five meters away. I saw how it happened. He flipped over and landed on the concrete of the front door entrance of the adjacent apartment.

I do not remember a sound. I only remember him lying there as if nailed on the cross—his arms wide apart. I had never seen a dead person before, but as a Catholic girl, I knew.

I knew that he was dead.

I remember thinking this is exactly like a dead person is meant to look. It was a curious and scientific thought, and I do not remember being shocked or frightened. I just felt calm, and that calmness did not leave me the whole day. Maybe I was in shock. Maybe I dissociated. Now, with the knowledge I have, I guess I had probably experienced both.

Everybody around me went into a frenzy. They called the ambulance, rushed to the hospital, talked to doctors, made phone calls, and then there was the moment when the final decision was to be made. They stopped those machines that kept him artificially alive. They said he would have never recovered from that accident to a life worth living.

Did I ask my mom any questions? Who was taking care of me? Where was I? And where was he?

* * *

They entered her body. Minutes before, she had tilted over on the operation table, the odor of anesthesia strong in her nose.

The metal blade of the scalpel flickered in the air and threw lightning flashes at the white, barren tiles of the emergency room. Then the scalpel sank into her soft flesh above the hip bone. The sharp cut made her body bleed. She did not see the blood. She did not see herself lying there on the operation table. She was far too young to remember, only three years old.

Her body did not forget. Her body knew through all those years that, once upon a time, it had been violated. That it had given up its vain and desperate attempt to stay conscious. She hadn't had a chance. The anesthesia did its job.

Many years later, as a young adult, that feeling of utter panic, helplessness, and an image of men and women in white coats rose to the surface of her consciousness. No way was she able to realize that it had to do with the operation back then, when she was only three. The memory of being invaded rumbled in her body, often causing nausea. Sometimes she passed out without knowing why. Now, some years later, she understood that a knot had been created in her neurological system, a furious convoluted Gordian knot which her body had tried in vain to get rid of. She understood now that her body had, all along, been aching for release of the memory in its cells and the tension this memory caused.

The process of remembering took only a few hours. It was a remembering of all the parts which she had lost back then at age three.

Anubis was with her all the time. She *knew* he was there, although she had not seen him, nor had she any words to talk to him. Without thinking, she had gone into the park near her house, had walked there on the lawn in ever-widening circles, listening to her heavy breathing, the only sounds she could perceive. She was in the *in-betweens,* as Erna would call it, in alien territory bereft of anything familiar. The only thing she knew was that she needed to continue walking in circles. She did not care what other people might think. If she had not kept moving, she would have collapsed on the green grass.

Then, after innumerable rounds, she noticed her breathing changing. It became lighter. She was on her way out. She returned from her underworld with new clarity of mind and an inner peace unknown to her before.

If she had not had the knowledge of him being with her, she would have been unable to stay in that land. She would not have managed to come full circle. He had been supporting her with his sheer presence. Her body had finally been granted the chance to dissolve the knot. It had been given all the time it needed to bring the shattered pieces of the mirror together so that she would become whole again.

* * *

"Nobody intended any harm," Clara said slowly.

Anubis only nodded.

"I must have felt so betrayed," she murmured. "I must have felt so desperately lonely. I must have been so afraid. Nobody knew. They were all . . . just . . . ignorant. Why should I not feel well in this place with other children and people who took care of my physical well-being? I must have been in such a terror."

"Terror, despair, and the feeling of being condemned to the core without knowing why."

Anubis had a distressed look on his face.

"Those are often the components for traumata, in particular regarding children who do not yet understand. There are so many experiences like yours, Clara. Wars, famine, terror—the settings differ, but the suffering is the same."

"I must have been so afraid," Clara repeated quietly.

"And remember," he said softly after a while. "Nobody intended any harm."

She smiled lightly, but then her face turned serious again. "What is this life all about? Why do we need to go through those experiences of ignorance? Is it so that we all become aware of what we are actually doing to each other? This world is crazy, it is crazy beyond imagination, and we slowly awaken from the dream, from this crazy, torturing dream. The awakening is painful, too. We see where we come from, and we see how far away we are still from a more benevolent future that we only glimpse. Glimpses of light, like fireflies in the dark."

Anubis stood and moved towards her. He gently pulled her out of her seat and wrapped his arms around her. "You are finding your way home," he whispered. "It has been a long way since you all tumbled into darkness. The veils are being lifted now. All those painful experiences come up in your consciousness so that you see what you have been doing to each other out of ignorance, of fear, of misperceptions."

He paused, then said, "The bridge over that abyss is your compassion for yourself, for the others, the compassion for the ignorant ones, the innocent ones, and the uninformed and unaware. It is a period of great pain, because all those emotions are making themselves known. You are in the process of crossing the abyss with the other end already in sight and with the old patterns still virulent and unresolved. It is a major challenge and also a major opportunity for growth, my love. And you have grown a lot. You still are growing. Growth is eternal. And the more you will grow into your real being, the more you will experience the bliss within you."

4

THE BELOVED

"Guess what!" Erna said, wide-eyed. "The Egyptians used to believe in nine spiritual bodies."

Clara turned and stared at her friend, unable to comprehend the meaning of her words. "Nine what?"

"Nine spiritual bodies!" Erna turned the page back to where she had started and began reading aloud. "The basis of the Egyptian art and science of the soul are the Nine Bodies of Light, also known as the Nine Eyes of Light. To the Egyptians, just as we have our physical body, so, too, do we have eight other bodies. They are just as real in other dimensions or wavebands of vibration. Igniting these nine was the journey of life and death: uniting them all was to enter into eternal life. This process was also called *Osirification*."

Erna's expression was a mixture of wonder and nuisance as she put down the book. "It is getting more complicated by the second," she moaned. "Who would understand all this?" She began to rapidly skim through the book again, her fingers frantically tracing the lines of text as she flipped through the pages.

"What are you looking for?" Clara asked cautiously.

Erna glanced at Clara, but did not respond as she kept searching the words.

Clara sighed. Erna could be like that: searching feverishly for her truth without stopping for a second, her cheeks reddened with heat, a crazy glint in her eyes. Usually, it took Erna quite some time to calm down and be accessible again.

This time, however, Erna slammed down the book after only a few minutes. "You need to talk to your Egyptian guy about this," she said fervidly. "It is most intriguing, but we need to have it broken down into the mirrors of nowadays life. Do you hear me, Clara? Nowadays life!"

Clara nodded and offered a soothing smile. "Okay, Erna. I will see what I can do. You must brief me, however. Otherwise, I won't know what to ask."

Erna leaned back into the sofa. "We will study this together." Her voice left no doubt of her determination. "This is extremely important stuff." She waved her friend to come nearer, and they both touched their heads together over the book.

* * *

"What are the nine spiritual bodies, Anubis?"

"They are holographic spheres of reality which exist within you. Some also call them *Keys to Ascension*."

"Ascension? Why?"

"Each of them represents a gateway to enlightenment. They all serve one purpose, Clara—that you may realize what you are in the deep. Igniting these nine is indeed the journey of life and death. Uniting them means entering eternal life. If you unite all parts, you will become a fully conscious human being, and your soul can be fully present. If you change one body of light, then all of them change.

"How can I explore those spiritual bodies?" Clara asked.

"Do you remember that sound seminar you went to?"

Clara nodded. Of course she remembered. How could she forget? Several hundred people had gathered in an impressive Venetian ballroom, and the air had been dense with the expectations of the audience. Slowly, the sound healer had started rotating the leather mallet around the giant, shimmering crystal bowl. The intense sounds of the crystal bowl rolled like deep waves into the room again and again, sometimes soft and gentle, sometimes penetratingly fierce. No one could escape those sounds. Clara had felt relentlessly enveloped by them. They had washed over her and moved into her with compelling vigor. Her eyes were closed, but when she opened them for a split second, her surroundings oscillated. After some moments, the sound healer began intoning with his voice, calling in the divine Egyptian beings by their names, one by one. Clara felt ravished. The power of his deep voice, together with the sounds of the crystal bowl, created shivers all over her body. Suddenly her heart opened at an incredible speed, and pure light streamed into her from above.

I do not understand, she thought. What is going on?

Only a few seconds later, she understood. A few seconds later, he began calling in Anubis. There was no doubt that something in her had felt his presence way before the teacher had voiced his name. She had sat there, mesmerized.

"Clara?" Anubis said to her now.

She turned around.

"Why did I perceive you *before* he intoned your name?" she asked in a hushed voice. "Why did I perceive such an incredible light? Is your name a gateway, too?"

"The sphere of sound or vibration is indeed one of the gateways, or holographic bodies," Anubis said. "The Egyptians called this gateway *REN*. They discovered that everything originates in sound, every thought, idea, or feeling. With each new feeling, you create a new sound. Your world is a world of sounds."

"So, it is your name which is a gateway?" Clara asked.

Anubis nodded. "As is yours," he said. "When you know your own true sound, you will know who *you* are. REN is one of the lenses through which you can become conscious of yourself."

Anubis paused, then added, "You know there are eight other lenses."

"How can I explore them?"

"You started the moment when you entered this world," he said. "It is a holographic exploration, an alchemical process to allow the full descent of light into your physical form. We are exploring this together, Clara. Your body is limited in its capabilities to adapt to new input. We will take it slowly. At the same time, the process is as fast as possible. When there is an opening, there is progress."

* * *

She remembered well when he called her *beloved* for the first time. He had looked into her eyes; two dark poles of light locked into hers as if no power of this world could separate them.

A few moments ago, they had both let their eyes rest upon the surface of the calm lake. It shimmered in a spectacular dark blue, much like the color Clara remembered from her swims in the Aegean sea when she had been a teenager. She always loved to dive and used to let herself sink deeply and then look up in awe of the luminescent rays of the sun breaking at the water's surface above her. She had always been enthralled by the oxygen escaping her mouth in silvery bubbles of air, enthralled by the way they graciously floated upwards.

Always, there was her longing to dissolve in this blue, to let her body gradually turn into pure water. Whenever she imagined it, bit by bit, it was most difficult to imagine her head dissolving. It would always dissolve last. Only when she gave a clear command would the desired image surf into her head—the image of her body being as blue as the water, the image of the blue sea empty, devoid of her body floating in it, but in some way still holding the memory of her. Or was her consciousness expanding immeasurably into the vastness of the water, liberated from her body, no more captured in the comparatively small space it usually takes up? Her mind could not provide her with an answer. However, the simultaneous sensations of emptiness and expansion had always enraptured her.

Clara sighed and looked up.

When their eyes met, he nodded. "You are starting to remember," he said. "Soon there will be a time when you understand much more about who you are and where you come from. The process is unfolding in more than just this dimension. At times, it will be scary. But you will master it, because you are discovering new sources of love and trust. I am not worried, my beloved, and you should not be too worried, either."

She stared at him, confused. "I do not feel worried," she finally said, though her voice belied her words.

His eyes appraised her. "So, what do you feel?"

She closed her eyes and tried to bring her full attention into herself. "I do not really know," she said vaguely. "Maybe numb. *Numb* might be the right word."

"Numbness is a sign that there is a part in you which is hiding, which is too afraid to wake up."

"Could I possibly wake up this part?" she asked.

"Any idea how?" Clearly, he wanted her to seek the answer within herself.

She stared at the ground, pondering his question.

"Where in your body do you feel the numbness?" he prompted.

"In my legs," she said after a while. "They feel sleepy. Also in my throat. It feels blocked."

"Can you stay present with both of those sensations?"

Clara nodded. When she focused her awareness into her legs, she realized with surprise that they wanted to kick something as hard as possible. But why?

She shifted the attention to her throat. Immediately, a feeling of helplessness overcame her. The image of a thick, dark ball with a woolen and sticky quality popped into her mind. Appalled, she told Anubis about it.

"If you had the freedom to shout through it, what would you shout?" he asked.

She brooded on this question for quite a while. How would shouting through it feel? It was as if shouting through whatever was there required a lot of pressure. Suddenly her face darkened. "It is too much for me!" she yelled.

Clara's shoulders sank, and she suddenly felt like sobbing. She thought, what is going on here? I am not yelling at *him*! Why am I so sad?

"That's it!" Delight filled his voice. "You hit it. You hit the feeling behind the block. How do you feel now, after the yelling?"

She looked up at him, anger, sadness, and surprise eddying through her. "I feel sad," she said, after some hesitation.

"There seems to be a small girl in me who feels totally overwhelmed. I feel sad for this child. And the sticky feeling in my throat is gone." Clara chuckled. "I did not know that I was having that thought." Her face warmed. "I feel a bit childish."

"Are you addressing anyone in particular with this thought?"

She shook her head. "Not really."

"It might be the part in you which is overwhelmed by too much input, such as from the news on your television. The more you open up to other realms of reality, the more your body takes in. Then there is resistance, and a knot is being created. Your throat might have wanted to say, 'Shut the fuck up!'"

"Anubis!" Clara scowled at him. "How can you say that?"

He laughed lightly. "Sorry. Maybe the throat wanted to say, 'Please be gentle with me. Don't override me.' One does become increasingly vulnerable with the opening up of the body."

His gaze was one of patient pride. "It is good to become aware of those knots. They are like a program running in the back of your mind. They influence your presence, your decisions, your way of interpreting life without you realizing it. When you tune into them, you change their vibration. You can release them, like you did when you yelled. What about your legs?"

"They want to kick and bang."

Anubis smiled. He lowered his long stick into the water and steered the canoe slowly back to the shore.

"What now?" Clara asked.

"Let them kick and bang!" he said lightheartedly. "Follow the impulse of your legs. A lot of anger might be stored there. Discharge that energy. You have been suppressing it for quite a long time. Now you can release it and return that energy to your own circle of power. Otherwise, it will continue to influence your way of seeing things and judging them. You might still hang out in victim mode although there is no reason to hang out there anymore. When you follow the original impulse of kicking, you can release that pattern on a physical level. Afterwards, there will be more clarity within you."

With a final push, he shoved the boat up onto the sand. "Test it!" he then said. "Your body needs to experience it. Otherwise, it will not know that it is real."

A question simmered in the back of Clara's mind, but she was too shy to ask. Finally she gave herself a push. "Why did you just call me 'beloved'?" she asked while climbing out of the boat.

He looked wicked for a moment. "I hope this is okay with you," he then said apologetically. "It slipped out."

How could it not *be okay for me?* She gazed at him, only realizing that very instant how much he meant to her. She was suddenly filled with inexplicable joy.

"We have already traveled a long and winding road together, Clara. We will be jointly walking into the future, if this is your will."

The two of them fell silent as tiny ripples of waves lapped at the shore.

"I feel very blessed to finally be walking this trail with you," he then added quietly.

* * *

"Have you told Marco about him?" Erna's expression appeared too innocent to be true. She took a sip of Coke. A frown had crossed her brow a moment ago when Clara told her about Anubis calling her his "beloved".

"No, of course not!" Clara said, crossing her arms. "You are the only person who knows about him, and that will remain carved in stone for the next few hundred years!"

She wrestled with the gigantic orange umbrella on her terrace. Its cord had been jammed in the spool, and the more she picked at different parts of the cord, the more entangled it became. With increasing impatience, she tore at the cord. The umbrella bent menacingly to the side, and the wooden crossbars made a screeching noise.

Erna laughed. "I would not bet on that," she said, more to herself. "You will not be able to hide *that* energy from anybody close to you. It is his presence which is being felt. Even I can feel it, and I tend to believe that I am as sensitive as a stone."

"Well, you know how Marco is." Clara glanced upwards into the umbrella's ceiling.

"No, I don't. You keep saying this, but as a matter of fact, I don't. You tell me he always complains and that you are not evolving together. Do you have an idea where *you* want to go with him? Do you happen to have a somewhat more mature vision for the two of you, such as a commitment to tune into each other's hearts once in a while?"

Clara lowered her arms and stared at Erna in disbelief. What had gotten into Erna? She thought grimly, how dare she talk to me like that!

Erna shrugged apologetically. "I only hear the usual blah-blah from you, my beloved friend," she said, deliberately stretching the word *beloved*. "I only hear that Marco does not talk about his feelings and that he is absorbed by his difficult job situation. Maybe it is *you* who needs to change vibrations for your relationship to thrive. More loving consciousness, I would call for! Besides, how much loving consciousness are you just bringing into your endeavor to fix this poor umbrella?"

Clara gasped, then lowered her head. Resolutely, she headed into the house and came back carrying a huge pair of loppers. "Now I do it the *Erna way!*" She held up the loppers to the entangled cord.

Before Erna could say a word, Clara vehemently cut the cord above the knot. The end of the cord slipped through the spool, and the umbrella collapsed with a swooshing sound. Both women startled.

Stunned, they looked up to the open sky.

"Freedom," Erna said dryly. "An alternative to be considered."

* * *

"Hi there," Clara said with much relief in her voice as she got up from the wooden seat. She'd been sitting there quite a while, her thoughts wandering while tension built up in her stomach. No waves curled the lake, its surface still and bleak. The boat sat there, motionless, only shifting when she moved to stretch her aching muscles. She had become increasingly desperate—where *was* he? Only the boat had floated there, waiting for her.

"Stay where you are." He waved his hands. "No need to get up. How are you?"

"Shaky." Her voice echoed the tremor she felt inside. "I am not sure if it is good that I am here. The more I look at this desolate lake, the more depressed I become."

He eyed her closely. She winced under his scrutinizing look.

"Stay with me," he said to her when she shied away. "You must trust me. You must trust the beings of the higher realm. Everything is for the best in you. You do not see it yet, because you still try to understand it from the perspective of the small ego self. It endeavors to control everything it can grasp. Do not go for this. Simply decide not to listen to the voice of your mind. It is a decision to believe in the good. It is a fierce one. Once you make this decision, everything will re-order itself accordingly. It is *you* who will be manifesting it."

Clara bowed her head and spoke with humility in her voice. "I am grateful that you are with me. Why do you spare your precious time with me at all?"

He sighed. "There is such a strong feeling of unworthiness in humanity. You immediately take on all this burden when you are being delivered into this world. It is an illusion. If you knew what you are in the deep you would stand here with shining eyes and a big smile in your face. I can see it in you."

Clara clasped her fingers together. "I do not feel at all like that gorgeous being you just described. I feel very unworthy of your attention. And I feel guilty because I fail in not seeing myself as that gorgeous being you describe. I am just a complete failure. Excuse me, Anubis. It is just the way it is."

"Do you notice something?" Anubis asked. "There is so much *I* in your words. In reality, there is no *I*. It is an artificial separation from oneness—in order for oneness to experience itself. It is a mirror you create to look into."

He made a fist with his hands.

"Destroy the mirror! Then create another. My eyes, for example. Use my eyes as a mirror! Look deeply into them, let the thoughts drop away, and see what happens."

Clara swallowed hard and gazed into Anubis's eyes. Dimly, she saw a miniature figure, herself, in the center. He nodded. "Keep your eyes steady," he murmered. His dark pupils seemed to magnetize her and draw her further into him. The outline of his face faded. Suddenly, there was a cracking noise inside of her head. She shuddered. And then she saw a woman sitting right in front of her, a woman with black curly hair and green eyes staring at her intently. Someone made an outcry of astonishment. Where did it come from? Clara's mind raced.

I cannot believe this, she thought. I seem to be behind his eyes! I am looking out of his eyes, watching myself sitting in front of him.

A feeling of claustrophobia overcame her, and she panicked. "I want to get out of here! Right now! Out of here!"

"Please stay." His voice was soft, gentle, like a tender caress. "Move into your heart."

Clara's heart thrummed in her ears so loudly she found it difficult to hear him.

"Please, Clara. Trust me and move into your heart."

She bit her lip. Maybe I can close those eyes, she suddenly thought, whoever's eyes they are. When she did, darkness settled in, and she calmed.

"Move into your heart, and imagine your heart opening up like the petals of a flower," Anubis said.

Clara had the sensation of a swaying in the center of her heart, as if a fragile blossom had been softly stirred by the wind. Then she perceived the image of a chrysanthemum opening up from its center slowly, petal by petal, revealing itself to some invisible presence lavishly, as if enjoying each gentle movement. It felt exquisite. At the same time, the opening made her feel vulnerable. There was an ever-expanding sweetness. It made her feel drunk.

This is all there is, she thought.

Waves of gentleness and calmness floated through her.

"This is all there is," Anubis said.

His words? Had she not thought those words an instant ago? Something inside her tensed.

At that moment, he whispered gently, "Drop deeper into the experience of me. Feel me! Take every minute of time you need and realize that there is no other. Everything is here in this moment. Everything."

Ecstasy rushed through her, lifted her up. At the same time, his gentleness anchored her deeply into this body. The sensations became stronger. A column of light reached far up above her and equally far below. She could not see either end of it. Then she gasped. She herself was this column of light! Or was it Anubis?

This is the most amazing experience I've ever had, she thought breathlessly. I feel so vast and open. And at the same time, so endlessly gentle and soft.

Then the cracking noise sounded again.

Bewildered, she opened her eyes. When she looked down, she saw her feet. She had returned to her body.

Clara rubbed her forefront. She felt dizzy. Questions were whirling in her head, but she could not find words to express them.

Finally, she managed to ask, "What was that?"

Anubis gazed at her as an amused smile played across his lips. "Do you still feel like a failure?"

"A failure?" The thought astonished her. Then she remembered and laughed. "I do not even know anymore what a failure is!"

He grinned. Then he turned serious again. "On a soul level, we are pure light stretching out through all dimensions. We are one with all that is," he said. "Through me, you experienced the oneness of things. The oneness of consciousness."

"So, where does this . . . feeling of . . . unworthiness . . . come from?" Clara's mind struggled to find the right words.

"These feelings are in your energy field. They are in the energy field of all human beings on this earth. They are not yours. The moment you identify yourself with them, the moment you believe you are those feelings, you are lost."

She beamed at him.

He smiled mischievously. "I am only here to help you realize this. You know, just to put you on another track."

Then his tone turned more pressing. "Believe me, Clara. When you undo those strings, your true being will begin to soar. You will notice it with each string you undo, each you loosen. The process is not without pain. It is important to do it gently, but gradually you will start to trust that it gets lighter and lighter."

* * *

"I explored the first spiritual body a bit," Erna said, smiling mirthfully where they both stood in Clara's kitchen the next day. "It is quite interesting what I found out. Do you want to hear it?"

Clara continued cutting a loaf of bread with a seemingly blunt knife and did not respond. She maltreated the bread with ostensible impatience.

"See!" Erna said "This is the first expression of the *KHAT*, the physical body."

Clara remained silent and kept forcing the dull knife into the bread. Then she stopped abruptly and looked up. "You want to say the physical body is one of the gateways?" she asked slowly.

"You are so hungry that you want to kill this poor piece of bread in front of you," Erna said cheerfully, ignoring her question. "This is the part of the body which is unconscious of itself. It is the *animal* in you!" She emphasized *animal* as if it was something detestable.

Clara groaned and waved a strand of hair from her face. "What are you saying? I have not eaten since you prepared that tea cup of a salad ages ago. Remember? I am starving!"

Erna stared at her and shook her head in disbelief. Then she laughed. "If you became conscious of the feeling of the knife in one hand and the soft bread in the other, you would move to a more evolved stage of the KHAT."

I could kill her! Clara clenched her hand around the knife so that her knuckles turned white. She did not utter a sound.

"The second stage is reached when we become aware of the information through our senses," Erna continued, annoyingly instructive. "This butter, for example—" she pierced one of her fingers into the golden lump in front of her, "—is soft because you left it outside the fridge last night." She smiled maliciously and then licked traces of the butter off her finger. "Mmmm. This is nice. See, I am in a much more evolved physical body than you are. I am aware of the smell, taste, and form of this piece of butter."

"Will you stop being so preposterous!" Clara shouted, pointing the knife towards her friend. "Otherwise, I am going to follow my 'animal instinct,' as you so nicely put it." She reached for the butter but could not quite grasp it, and it slipped out of her hands. With a soft thud, it fell onto the tiled floor and lay there like a battered pancake.

"The third stage is much more difficult to grasp," Erna said, pretending not to notice what had just happened. She rubbed her nose reflectively.

"In the third stage of your evolved physical body, you realize that you are part of the earth, and the earth body and your body are one. You understand that, if the earth were not there, you would not be there, either. You know, at a deeper level, that you are nothing without the earth. So, in a way, if there were no butter . . ." her voice dwindled ". . .*you* were not there, either."

Clara bent down to scoop up the butter, leaving a greasy smear behind.

"Apparently, it is all about the big heart," Erna murmured. "The indigenous people talk about this, also." Distracted, Erna stared out the window. Outside, the evening sun hovered above the tall neighborhood buildings. Then her eyes grew large.

"The big heart?" Clara asked, her gaze searching for whatever it was Erna was staring at outside the window. The sun had become a giant orange disk bathing the buildings of the city around them in its late afternoon light. The beauty of it was breathtaking.

"Yes," Erna said. "Apparently, you could also say that it's the pulse of the heart of the earth. We are continuously being pulsed by her heart. I guess this is the only reason we experience being alive at all, here on this planet. If I understand rightly, this is one of the most important teachings within the context of the physical body: our connection, or indeed our oneness, with this earth." She sighed. "I am not so sure whether I will ever understand this."

"Never." Clara gave her friend a malicious smile. She playfully slapped her on the shoulder. "I would suggest that you wipe the floor while I prepare a mega cheese sandwich for the two of us. Then I will tell you what this is all about, okay? No human being is lost forever, and we might even experience some spiritual evolution with this one here!"

Ignoring Erna's huffing, Clara turned with a giggle to retrieve plates from the cupboard.

* * *

Clara opened her eyes and stared into darkness. Her body had violently jolted, and the movement had awakened her. Now her eyes were darting anxiously around the room. *Calm down. Breathe and calm down,* she ordered herself, but her mind struggled to obey.

She glanced at the neon green numbers of her alarm clock. Four thirteen in the morning. Another night of rest cut short.

"Help!" she pleaded silently. "Anubis, please help."

Her outcry seemed unnoticed as she stared into the dark night.

With rising desperation, she thought, where are you?

Still, there was no answer. Silence rolled over her in mighty black waves. She was alone.

Something within her shrank as the weight of utter loneliness pressed upon her. She closed her eyes, and forlorn desolation settled on her like an icy blanket of nothingness, a dark woolen cloth with no holes, no exits, just complete isolation. Her mind raced as she searched for methods to stop this overwhelming rush of alienation, stop this state of being from becoming the only valid reality in this moment. Her head spun, and when she opened her eyes, the room tilted around her.

"Please," she heard herself saying in a pressed voice.

Then she recalled something Anubis had said about people being stuck in their pleading states. With a last defiant struggle, she sat up.

"No!" she said loudly, her voice cutting through the night. "No." She would not let this feeling sweep over her and pull her down to the bottom of the ocean.

She repeated her *no* even more vehemently, and then she shouted it out.

A deep growling sounded within her. It made its way up from her belly, into her throat and left her mouth in a long, deep, "Nooooooo!" The strong force of the sound vibrated through her body and made her skin tingle. It was as if the word had filled the void inside her with its bottomless and tenacious sound.

Everything came to a halt. As if she had pulled the emergency brake in a speeding train, the spinning world around her righted itself. The last final noises of the train sliding to a stop screeched around her, then quietness—complete quietness beyond mere silence—filled her with the sensation of utter presence.

When she was, at last, out of breath, she began to hum, "No."

The melody she created reminded her of a lullaby. She listened to her own gentle voice meandering through the night. Nothingness pervaded everything, but this time, the nothingness was different because it moved through her instead of separating her from the outside world.

How could I forget! This moment is all there is.

Everything else was already gone or yet to be experienced in a future moment in life.

Clara breathed out a long and relaxing breath. A question turned up in her head, a question which had obviously found its way around the barriers of the isolated fortress which was her mind, a question that had slipped through a tiny gap of this nothingness and into her awareness.

It was inaudible but crystal clear.

How much love do I allow in?

She held her breath.

Something in her opened, and the opening grew larger at an enormous speed. It was as if a hole at the horizon had given up its resistance and let in the universe, and the universe took its chance and rushed in carelessly, fervidly, full of passion and life force. Clara's body began to vibrate deeply, and she realized with amazement how much her body had yearned for this opening.

How much do I allow in? she wondered again. Her heart

pounded stronger and harder until she worried it might burst out of her chest.

Will this be too much for me?

The strong notion rose within her to somehow stop the flooding, somehow let the expansion come to an end.

"It is not possible," she cried out as horror rose in her mind. The expansion was irrevocable. Something in her continued to expand at an incredible speed.

At that moment, she realized she was not alone. A familiar presence emerged right beside her bed, and though he remained invisible to her this time, his existence was palpable. She let out a pent-up breath.

"This is the portal, Clara," she heard him murmuring. "Do not hold yourself back. You will lose the sacredness of this experience. Let yourself be dissolved into the opening."

She flinched. "I do not like to be washed out," she whispered.

"I know," he said quietly. "It feels like annihilation, doesn't it? And yet, it also is the antidote to the feeling of being overwhelmed by the fullness and diversity of life. Stay open, my love. Annihilation, or nothingness, and the state of being overwhelmed are the two extremes you have to come to terms with here on this planet. When you have mastered the two on the physical plane, you know that you have gone a long way towards wholeness. Come on, my love, let us both journey together through this opening."

She closed her eyes. Was he wrapping his arms around her? It felt like it. The image of a jigsaw surfaced in her head, a jigsaw with her standing on top of it, at the pivot point, with her legs spread apart. She wobbled and frantically tried to regain her balance, fearing annihilation and her equally immense resistance to being overwhelmed. Her legs started to shake, first lightly, then stronger. She knew she would not be able to endure the tear much longer. She had to give up! She spread her arms and let herself fall back into the void. Only then did she realize that he still had his arms wrapped around her. She let herself be carried away, into a deep and healing sleep.

5

EGYPTION ENCOUNTERS

The next time she met him at the lake, she knew exactly what to ask.

"Anubis," she said impatiently. "Will you ever dare to show yourself in my part of the world? Or will you just keep whispering mysterious messages into my ears? It does not always need to be this cave, does it?"

He laughed merrily and shook his head. "I did not have the impression it was *me* preventing our meetings in your reality," he said. "You can meet me wherever you want. In your apartment, in your kitchen, in your bedroom, wherever!"

Now it was her turn to back up. "Excuse me," she said, propping her hands on her hips. "Why should I invite you into my house? There must be another place to meet for the first time in the real world. Don't be so pushy."

He pretended to sigh. "Okay," he said, giving in. "What about meeting in your favorite café? On neutral ground, so to say?"

"That's a good idea!" She clapped her hands. "Let's meet at the Café L´Intro. I will give you the address."

He smiled. "No need for that. Just call me, and I will be there."

"What do you mean, 'Just call me?'"

The airiness of his answers still confused her.

"Come on, my love. This is the way to connect with beings like me. You should know this by now. Tune into their vibration by invoking their name, open yourself to the possibility of meeting them—even if the opening is only a millimeter—and then wait and see."

"Some people wait and see for ages," she said, pursing her lips. "I will give you my mobile number, just in case."

He shook his head again and laughed. "Right you are," he said. "Some wait for centuries. They are enjoying their pleading state, because they fear what would rush into them if they opened up a bit. 'Please, please, please,' they say all the time. 'Please show yourself to me, although I know that I am not worthy to be with you.' They are so much entangled in their feelings of unworthiness. It is as if Jesus and Mary Magdalene were arriving at a hotel where there is a sign that reads *Rooms Available,* but the reception desk is closed. 'Sorry, my Lord and Lady, we are busy praying to you.' No wonder they do not feel the army of angelic beings surrounding them, waiting for the tiny opening to present themselves. It would be hilarious, if it were not so sad."

He sighed.

"Do not worry. You know how to open yourself so that you become aware of me and my friends around here. Not to mention the glorious being within you, call it angel, light being, or something else. It is a welcoming and a dropping into the numerous possibilities which might enfold. Trust yourself, Clara. I will be there. I am always there."

She sat, pensively watching him. "You know what?" she slowly said. "Let us meet in my apartment. I feel more safe there than in public. How should we possibly talk in a café, anyway? People will think I am mad if they see me babbling to myself. When I next call you, I will invite you to have a seat on my newly bought sofa."

He smiled. "I promise to behave," he said mockingly. He sank his stick into the water. The boat slowly turned around, and they headed back to the shore.

* * *

Clara's mouth opened in awe when he finally turned up. She had not really given it much thought, actually. Neither had she prepared herself. For hours, she had watched the white disc of the full moon moving along her window pane. Wrapped in a blanket, she curled in her armchair and sipped some tea. Airy sounds from the *Lightship* CD wove through the room, dancing to flickering light from the glowing logs burning in her fireplace. She sank deeper into her chair and sighed, enjoying the peace and serenity of her surroundings. Her wandering thoughts had a crystal-clear quality to them. Her head felt light and strangely bigger than usual.

Suddenly, she heard his voice, strikingly dark. "Would you like me to come forward now?"

His voice vibrated within her body, resonating in her heart and womb and all the way down her legs and into her toes. It was a sweet and strong vibration, as if every cell had awakened and became alive and vibrant.

"You do. I can feel it," he said with amusement in his voice. "Will you please confirm, Clara? I do not like to be too much of an intruder."

She did not respond at first. Why did he have such an effect on her body? Yes, she wanted him here, wanted to see him as a real being, as real as anybody out there on the streets of Munich. Then, on the other side, what if it were all different then? If the magic just evaporated? If he were just a guy like any other guy here in this city?

"Clara?" she heard him asking.

She grimaced. "Do I have a choice, really?" she asked.

"You always have a choice. It is your birthright. There might be others trying to convince you of the opposite. I will be gone in a moment, if you so wish."

Her body tensed. "You are welcome," she said, and her voice cracked. Then she smiled. "Will I ever be alone again?"

"Yes and no," he said cheerfully. "Whenever there is an opening within you, I might present myself to you. You will always be able to close those gateways, Clara. As a matter of fact, you have done that for the last hundreds of years. The choice will always be yours. Let me just say, for the record: the process of *opening* is the challenge for you and those like you, not the closing."

The air stirred visibly in front of her, and then sparkles of blue light surrounded a dark body.

There you are! You're as dark as the night sky reflecting the moon so that I can just about recognize you. Amazing! I am not even afraid of you. I am full of trust.

The fire in the fireplace flared, illuminating Anubis in a most unusual costume, and Clara gasped at his appearance. He wore a knee-length dark blue skirt with golden metallic threads woven into it. A small row of hieroglyphs in blue and red decorated the front of his silken white T-shirt. His human face had three stripes of gold, red, and blue painted diagonally across the cheeks. His hair was staked in a long funnel, giving him a majestic appearance. He held the Ankh symbol, and his black leather sandals were stitched with still more symbols Clara didn't recognize. He stood motionless, impressive in his powerful grace.

Clara felt intimidated. Searching for her voice, she said humbly, "You look awesome, Anubis! Are you going to a ceremony?"

"I am celebrating one of your successful passages through your own underworld," Anubis said.

She looked at him questionly.

He did not respond, but he slowly moved towards her. Then he bowed down to her. "Thank you for receiving me here," he said in a reverential tone. "I feel very honored to be with you. I am here to serve you, Clara."

She gazed into his dark eyes. The colors in his face became fuzzy, as if they were fusing into each other. The atmosphere intensified, and Clara shifted uneasily. Was she expected to say something now?

"Please sit down." She motioned towards the sofa opposite her. "I guess I should offer you a drink."

"That would be wonderful," he said, stepping back. He pursed his lips and tilted his head, obviously noticing her confusion. "I'll have what you always have with this friend of yours. What is her name?"

Clara was speechless. "Coke," she then mumbled. "No, I mean Erna."

"Okay," he said, smiling. "I'll have some Erna then."

Clara opened her mouth, closed it, and shook her head. "I'll get you some Coke."

When she put the glass down in front of him and moved over to her seat again, his eyes sparkled with admiration and curiosity. Was he waiting for her to make the next move?

She was amazed when she heard herself blurt out, "Anubis, tell me—do you exist? I mean, are you real? I am struggling so much with the thought of you being a—a—a *whatever!*"

He looked at her reflectively. "What if you touch me?" he then asked softly. He slowly raised a hand towards her.

Clara backpedalled, and his smile disappeared.

"I am sorry," he said with dark eyes. "It must be confusing for you. Where I come from, this is as real as the world you consider real."

She did not know what to do. She recalled her amazing experience of touching his human face a while ago, down there in that cave. That was, however, in a meditative state! In the dreamtime, as far as she understood.

But now he was here, in her apartment, in this most unusual outfit.

She deeply longed to trust him. But what if her hands just passed through his, as if through a ghost? She would be petrified and, at the same time, devastated with disappointment.

"I understand," she heard him saying. "It is okay."

She looked away. She knew he was right. But her fear was real, too. No, she was not ready for this. Not yet.

Finally, she looked back at him. His eyes had a yearning, even hungry look. She had never seen him looking at her like this. The muscles in her neck tensed. At the same time, a rush of energy coursed through her body.

"I sense your despair," he said seriously at that moment. "It has every right to be there, Clara. Please do remember, though, that you are the physical manifestation of a much vaster being. Remember the angel!"

She stared back at him.

"You and your fellow humans are called to transform in a very short time. Actually, time itself undergoes transformation. I can see you being torn between your divine self, which you are becoming more and more aware of, and your physical self, which has long been the only reality for you on this miraculous planet."

He fell silent for a moment. His face looked strained.

"It is scary," he then said. "It is an ever-widening crack you all need to bridge. It is an immense stretch. The tension you feel is your growing knowledge of your *belonging* to realities other than this one. Stay present with the tension, my love, and do not let yourself be overwhelmed by your confusion about what is real and what is not. Gather your courage, and explore it!"

"Is this what the Egyptian lightbodies are all about?" Clara asked slowly.

He offered a caring smile, then nodded. "It is an integrative process. You become conscious of the fact that your lightbody and your physical body are inexplicably intertwined. You increasingly become sensitive to their constant permeation of each other. When you dream of love, for example, your lightbody uplifts your physical body. It also works the other way around."

"I do not understand," she said incredulously. "What do you mean, the other way around?"

He looked at her with shiny eyes. Then he pointed to the sofa.

"Would you like to lie down for an experiment?"

She slowly got up and went over to the sofa. Then she pulled a blanket towards her and stretched herself. She closed her eyes and exhaled deeply, then opened them. "Go ahead!"

"Now *you* are impatient!" Anubis grinned. He sat in the chair opposite her. "Close your eyes again, and try to stay awake. I can see you are tired now, so this will be a challenge."

Clara obeyed and closed her eyes again.

"Can you feel your body lying on the sofa?" Anubis asked quietly.

Clara nodded.

"Move into your body with your consciousness. Try to imagine that your consciousness meanders into every part of your body. Envision yourself filling all spaces of your body with your consciousness. Take your time, and then tell me what you notice."

"I am becoming lighter," Clara answered after a while. "It is as if my consciousness goes into the furthest corners of my body and makes everything bright and shiny."

"Any dark areas?" he asked casually.

Clara scanned her body, then she shook her head. "I am not aware of any," she mumbled. "They are being pushed out by my consciousness."

"Good," Anubis said. "If you do this more often during the day, you become conscious of each and every part of your body and how you are currently integrating those higher frequencies into your body. At some point, you will experience these higher frequencies as one unified spinning sphere of multiple dimensions around and within your body—which is what you really are."

He smiled lightheartedly. "In those higher dimensions of the light, touch is as real as in your three-dimensional reality. There will be no difference for you, whether you meet me in the physical or in the ethereal realms. Your body will feel and know my touch as surely as you can see me right now, in these ceremonial clothes, here in front of you."

Exhaustion settled around Clara. It had all been too much. Her head started to spin, and she knew she would fall asleep in a moment.

The next morning, she awoke still lying on her sofa, wrapped in the blanket. When she opened her eyes, her living room seemed to brim in a surreal atmosphere. Had she not seen the familiar rooftops of her neighboring houses in front of her windows, she would have thought that the room had been transported to a faraway and strange place, to the top of the Himalayas, where snow and howling winds were the only real forces around her.

The atmosphere in her room was so unreal that she needed to pinch erself to make sure she did actually exist.

* * *

"I am so very excited," Clara sang, dancing barefoot on her stony terrace, her hips moving lavishly to the left and to the right. "I am so excited!"

"I can see it, my love," Anubis said, smiling. He stood at the doorway, scrutinizing the azure Bavarian sky as if he were searching for an answer to a hidden question. There was not a single cloud in the sky. The air was crisp, an indication that the cooler days of autumn were not far away.

"Do not worry," he finally said. "You'll be fine."

"I am not worried! I received so many nice compliments for the latest layout of this client's brochure. Now I want to give my best. I want to do everything to demonstrate to them that I am a very creative person," she said feverishly.

"I know," Anubis said. "It is nice to get so much attention, isn't it?"

"Yes," she said, beaming. "I am overflowing with excitement." She stopped dancing. "Well, at least a part of me is."

"Oh, only a part of you?" Anubis asked, amused. "What about the other parts?"

She furrowed her brow. "There is a small part within myself which is afraid to fail," she said hesitantly. "It's a part that is afraid of dreaming too big, a part which holds memories of the rise and the subsequent hard fall onto the harsh ground of realities. I want to protect myself. On the other hand . . ."

She gazed up into the blue sky, opening her arms as wide as she could. "On the other hand, I want to fly, to fly as high as the wildest bird in the sky." She closed her eyes and whirled around several times. Then she paused again.

"You seem to be split in two, my love," Anubis said. "Or possibly more than two."

"Yes," she confirmed after a few seconds.

Slowly, her body began to loosen up. "Yes," she repeated. "I am split in two: one part is dancing ecstatically on the waves of the big ocean, and the other part is afraid of being lured into its depth and being drowned in feelings of unworthiness, big ego identity, and megalomania. It is the little child in me wanting to feel worthy of honor. It is the *grown-up critic* in me warning me to not fly too high, wanting to protect me from the fall. How can I possibly reconcile those two forces?"

"You live in a world of duality, my love," he answered after a few moments. "Whenever one side of reality appears, there is bound to be the other side somewhere out there. Or better . . ." Anubis paused, "somewhere within you."

Absentmindedly, he moved his hands over the table to pick up some invisible bread crumbs which had escaped Clara's eyes. She had eaten an early breakfast with Erna this morning, and cups and plates were still waiting to be cleared up.

The sun warmed Clara's bare arms. A gentle breeze came up and cooled her skin. Soft wind rattled through the leaves of the giant chestnut tree in front of her apartment.

"This other side is hidden right now," Anubis added. "It is the shadow of all things. When it comes out, it ferociously calls for integration. Its whole purpose is to become one with its counterpart so that they can both merge back into the full picture of the puzzle of your life."

Anubis looked deeply into Clara's eyes, as if to check whether he should continue speaking.

She succumbed to his loving gaze.

How much she enjoyed being in contact with him! His eyes always invited her to dive deeper into the essence of her own being, while at the same time she felt as though she were lovingly being held, held by the presence of those shining mirrors of his.

The deeper I fall into those eyes, she thought, the more bliss I experience within me.

She knew it had not always been like that. The depth and the falling into the void had made her very much afraid. Giving up control was one of the hardest lessons she had faced in her life. Gradually and with practice, she had learnt to relax and to welcome whatever came up in that process. Then there was the moment she would never forget. It was not even a moment, it was a glimpse of a moment, but this glimpse was filled with the sweetest ecstacy, a pull of energy starting from below her belly button, her shaman center, as she understood it to be afterwards. It went all the way up to her breasts, through her throat, and right into the center of her head.

When she experienced the flow of energy for the first time, she thought it was the only feeling worth being born on this earth. She also thought it was the only feeling worth dying for. In dying, she somehow knew she would fully surrender to this feeling.

Since that glimpse of a moment in time, she shivered in anticipation whenever he offered those eyes to her—his eyes and the invitation to further explore those depths of melting into oneness.

"It is the teaching of Amun-Ra," he said, interrupting her reverie. "It seems to be the right time to tell you about Amun-Ra, my love. Have you ever heard of Amun-Ra?"

"Not really," Clara answered vaguely as she looked at him expectantly. "Tell me about him. Or is he a she, Anubis?"

Anubis looked out into the vast sky. His eyes were like two shiny silvery disks, little suns themselves. His voice trembled slightly when he began to speak. "Close your eyes, Clara. I will tune into the energy of Amun-Ra. You will pick up the vibration. Notice the shift of the energy field. Feel the energy of Amun-Ra. Together, we will reinforce the vibratory field." Anubis stood motionless.

The wind had stopped its play with the leaves. Clara closed her eyes and concentrated on her breathing. The sounds had quieted, as if someone had placed a cushion on everything.

Then Anubis started humming. It was a deep and guttural sound, and while it became stronger, it seemed to be coming from all directions, pervading everything.

Clara held her breath. The humming was powerful, and it also anchored her within herself, as it was so deep. Then the sound changed. It turned into a high-pitched tone. Clara began to feel uneasy.

In that moment, Anubis spoke. "Can you feel how powerful the energy is, Clara? It is the power of the sun; it is pure solar energy, the driving force of transformation. Focus on the sun with your third eye and feel its radiant power. Can you feel it?"

"Yes," Clara answered with her eyes still closed. Although the high tone had stopped, it still rang in her ears. It even seemed to become more forceful.

"There is a very strong power," she said slowly. "It is nearly unbearable, so strong it is."

"Yes," Anubis nodded. "Now I want you to focus on an equally strong force which is located at the back of the sun. It is dark—dark and invisible—but it is also part of the sun. It is the night side, the hidden side, the one we do not see when we look up into the sky. Let us tune into it now, while at the same time holding the focus on the solar side of the sun."

Clara jerked back as she experienced the powerful sensation of a very dark and forceful mass directly behind the sun. The impression was so puissant that she shivered. Then she willfully relaxed and tried to hold both sides of the sun in her awareness.

"How do you feel?" Anubis asked.

"It is amazing," she said after a little while. "When I feel the power of the light and the dark side at the same time, the power of the sun seems to multiply incredibly. It also feels much more . . . whole! And although the power is so much stronger, it feels easier to handle. It is such a . . ." She searched for the right word without success.

"Relief?" Anubis suggested.

"Yes," she said. She let out a deep breath. "It is such a relief to not only be aware of the sun's *bright* light."

"This is the power of the light and the dark when they are both being held in your consciousness," Anubis explained. "Amun-Ra is the expression for this wholeness, with Ra being the solar energy and Amun its dark side. Only when the two are one in consciousness can wholeness take place. If you suppress the dark, you do not have access to its powers."

"How do I become aware of the dark side of things?" Clara asked.

"Set your intent. Even if you do not recognize it, know it is there and connect with it. The dark side of things, the powerful hidden side, will make itself known when you open up to the simple fact that it exists. No need to *do* anything with it."

Clara's mind raced. Before she could voice another question, Anubis continued talking.

"You give relationships an impulse to change just by focusing on the unconscious. It is an invitation into other dimensions. Those relationships become deeper, less superficial."

"But how do I know what is in the other person's subconsciousness?" Clara asked.

"You do not need to know. Acknowledge its existence without judgements. Don't be surprised when there is a decisive shift in the other person. When you are in your heart, whatever wants to reveal itself can do so in a loving way."

"Could you please give me an example?"

"Do you know of a hyperactive person?" Anubis asked.

"Sure." Clara suddenly thought of her boss at work.

"When you are with a person who is hyperactive, who runs around like a headless chicken trying to cope with many things at the same time . . . know that it is the unseen and unresolved that drives this person. When you connect with this side, there is a space opening up both within you and the other person. You could say you welcome the dark side of this person to let itself be revealed and merge with the light of consciousness."

Anubis smiled.

"The person might suddenly collapse onto a chair and finally get some rest. It is a healing and powerful practice. Open yourself and be receptive to whatever might happen without trying to control it."

"How does this relate to my fear of being a failure," Clara asked tentatively.

"Hold both your fear as well as the joy in your awareness," Anubis said. "Let the two powers merge in front of your inner eyes. Then experience the change of your level of power."

The two sat there, listening to the wind and holding in their minds' focus the unified light and dark aspects of Amun-Ra.

Clara was wide-awake. I could sit here endlessly, she thought at some point. With him, I could sit endlessly. I would not miss anything. The world is inside me, ready to be explored.

Then an impulse rose within her, and without a moment of reflection, she followed it.

She jumped up.

"Time to get us a drink," she said. She grabbed her glass and ran into the kitchen.

* * *

Shards of light were flitting on the lake's unruffled surface. They appeared as a thousand tiny diamonds, enticing Clara with their joyful dance as she followed their movements with her eyes. There was longing for more, but she could not quite grasp it.

"How can I be more connected to the divine, Anubis?" she finally asked.

"There is nothing you can do against it," Anubis said from the front of the boat. "You are made of that power which you just called *divine*. The more you dream it, the more you will become conscious of its reality."

She chewed on her lips, then frowned.

"May I tell you something?" she asked shyly.

"Sure, my love," he replied. "Always."

"Before I met you today, I asked myself how I imagine divine power to be . . . which qualities it might have if it were to serve me . . . to fully bring me into my power."

She paused and her face grew warm. "You know, I imagined it to be . . . shameless. Shameless, raw, strong and also . . . loving. Present all the time. I imagined it to provide me with everything I need at each precise moment."

She rubbed her eyes. Those glittering sparkles of light dazzled her, and when she finally turned away from them, there were dark spots in her vision. "When I connected with this power—"

"When you became aware that you *are* that power," he interrupted her softly.

"Yes, I mean, yes . . . I suddenly got the strength to tune into you and meet you here at this lake, although I was actually very tired. The power was there, you know? How could this be?"

"With your question about how you imagine divine power to be, you set your intent to explore it. You created a space within yourself for it to move into you. Sekhem does not wait to be asked twice. It is there, when it is called."

"Sekhem?" Clara asked.

He nodded. "The Egyptians named this power *Sekhem*. It is one of the nine gateways to the light. Sekhem is pure life force. It is a fierce power. It can be shameless, reckless, full of passion and bliss. It calls upon you to live to your highest potential and not to compromise."

Clara shuddered. Although she was fascinated by what he'd said, she also felt intimidated.

"There is a price to pay, though," Anubis explained.

"What is it?" Clara asked breathlessly.

"You need to give up your restricted beliefs about freedom, security, and sexuality."

Clara whipped around to face him.

"What?" she asked, her eyes opening wide.

He nodded gravely, but his eyes betrayed him; they were full of delight.

"You are asked to dissolve whatever might be in the way, to experience true freedom, so that you become fluid and transparent. Then Sekhem will make its way into you. The less you resist, the easier."

"I am not sure whether I am ready for that," Clara moaned.

Anubis squinted. "You have already heard the calling." He pointed towards the glittering lake. "How do you want to stop the longing in order to be part of the flickering light?"

He smiled.

"Imagine the possibilities," he added, with a mysterious tone in his voice.

"There will be no shame, no fear, no holding back. Imagine the love, the joy, and the freedom."

* * *

"Why are those Egyptian divine beings and their myths at all relevant to us humans nowadays?" Clara asked with a doubtful voice as she looked up into the horizon. Low shreds of clouds moved around like flocks of sheep, pushing patches of blue to the sides, collecting them, separating them again.

No rationale there, Clara thought randomly. At least no rationale I am able to figure out.

She sighed.

"Here I am, a modern woman of the twenty-first century, discussing with you—the God of Funerary rites—my little, or not so little, worries of the day, and you give me some most invaluable insights into the true nature of things. So I gather. But why?" She shook her head.

"You are on your path to enlightenment, my love, whether you are conscious of it or not," he responded. "For this to take place, the spirit world needs to interpenetrate all spheres of your existence. The ancient Egyptians knew that. Their culture was infused with religious awareness. Your vision is being limited by those clouds whose existence prevent you from being aware of the sky. When you let the sky penetrate all your patterns and experiences, you know where to go. I am just someone to remind you of this."

Clara was silent for a while. Then she looked up at him. "It seems like an immense task."

"Don't worry. You are on the acceleration line."

He smiled.

"Each teaching opens lodges within you whose contents you are starting to remember. Soon we will work with symbols and geometric bodies. That will also quicken you."

"Symbols and geometric bodies?" Clara asked.

Anubis nodded. "The symbols of the Egyptians are very powerful. They are as powerful today as they were in those ancient times. The pyramid of Giza is one of the most powerful geometrical figures on this earth. Just imagine yourself standing right in the center of this gigantic pyramid. You will immediately notice an effect on your body. All this ancient knowledge about sacred geometry is now surging up. It is being revealed to whoever is ready to listen and see. You will gradually be able to use this knowledge for your own spiritual progress, Clara. Then you will always be aware of the blue sky on a rainy day. You will actually know that you *are* the blue sky."

* * *

Clara sat in front of her notebook, staring intently at the screen with burning eyes. A faint pulsing throbbed at her temples, and she knew she had to quit her research. Otherwise, she risked getting a splitting headache within the next hours.

Suddenly she heard his voice.

"We are all serving her," he said, his tone of voice deeply reverential.

Surprised, she looked up. Her eyes fell onto the filigrane Japanese tea pot on her desk. It had been quite a while since she had poured steaming hot water onto those tea leaves. The steam had long been gone, but the tea had remained undrunk, a dark brown liquid which had certainly turned bitter by now.

Outside, the day had given way to the night. The bright sky had turned into a deep blue, like ink being dropped into a glass of water. Clara had not noticed it; reading about Egyptian deities had absorbed her.

"What do you mean?" Clara asked. She turned around to face him. He stood right behind her, gazing out the window, lost in the city's spectacular skyline. There was a heaviness in his voice which had startled her. He stood motionless, the fine lines of his face carved in stone, it seemed. If she had not seen a tiny muscle pulsating at his temple, she could have sworn he was a statue, one of those antique stone statues on display at the Munich Museum of Egyptian Art.

"All Neters are serving Ma'at, the Goddess of the Heart," he said. "We are all in service to her. She is the supreme energy. She is the womb where we all come from and where we all return. She is the Great Mother."

He briefly bowed his head. "She is the one you meet when you have crossed the threshold of death. It is in the Hall of Ma'at, where you face her with the forty-two high beings representing rules of utmost integrity and look at all of your life experiences from the point of view of your heart, your *AB* soul. It is Ma'at who is preceding the ritual of the weighing of your heart against the feather of her crown to see whether you are allowed into the heavens of the Neters."

Clara shivered. "I will never be allowed in there," she said in a thin voice. "I will never be good enough."

He only looked at her passionately.

"See," he said—and for a split second, an expression of pain flickered across his face, before it turned blank again. "This is the *not-good-enough* vibration. It is like a chain tying you firmly to the lower levels of your being. You are the one chaining yourself to it. As long as you believe in this thought pattern, you will never be able to raise higher in consciousness."

He looked at her intensely.

"Just imagine how life on earth would be if people honored themselves for what they truly are: divine souls incarnated into a human body. Imagine if they walked around knowing that they never were anything other than pure and innocent.

"Clara," his voice turned emphatic, "I tell you there are more souls entering the heavens than you would imagine. It does not mean those souls had not done wrong during their span of life on this earth. They had their experiences, had caused harm, and suffered from the consequences. However, when you fully acknowledge your responsibility, you initiate an alchemical process within your heart which transforms everything. This is what it means to be fully responsible for all you are and all you have done."

"What will happen when I stand in front of Ma'at?" she asked cautiously.

"You will be seeing with your inner eye all the situations and people you have not made peace with yet—everything which is still rumbling in your subconscious. You will have the opportunity to make peace with them right at that very moment, and equally important, to forgive yourself and make peace with yourself."

Anubis's face lit up as he spoke.

"How does this sound?" he then asked, carefully watching Clara's face.

"Scary and consoling at the same time," she answered. "It seems like a huge task, too. Is there anything I could do to facilitate the process?" She frowned. "I guess Erna would ask whether I could sort of collect some brownies on the way—I mean, before the end?"

"You could start forgiving yourself right now, for example," Anubis suggested, smiling. "Is there anything for which to forgive yourself?"

"Lots!"

"In forgiving, there is an opening. It is one of the biggest challenges for you. Your story of Adam and Eve—their alleged eternal sin and subsequent expulsion from Paradise—is your chain and also your justification for living in guilt throughout all times. You, as a German, perfectly inherited the sin and guilt pattern. It is toxifying, this pattern. If your grandfather had not died in this accident, he would have died later from cancer. He did not know how to forgive himself. Therefore, he could never face those people he had been expelling from their homes and ask them to forgive him, not even silently."

After a moment, he said, "Not forgiving oneself is hell. It is eternal condemnation. It makes no difference whether you think it is a distant God who is condemning you or whether you yourself are doing it. You and God or the Goddess are one. The vibration is the same. It toxifies your soul and body."

Anubis turned silent, then he asked, "Can you imagine being without guilt?"

Clara closed her eyes. What did he just say: her being without guilt? It was as if she was rummaging through her body for a place which felt innocent.

"Do not search for it," he said in a hushed tone. "Be it!"

Clara immediately recognized what it meant to *be* innocent. Immediately. A rush of light energy went through her body from the feet upwards. She felt uplifted, as if she might rise towards the ceiling. A childlike, joyous giggle came out of her mouth. So *that* is the vibration of innocence, she thought. *I recognize this!.*

"Now, switch again to the heaviness of your guilt," Anubis said.

Something within Clara dropped down, like an elevator which moved down and then came to a halt. Ground floor, she thought, half amused and half desperate. She opened her eyes.

"You have the choice," Anubis said with an odd expression on his face. "Know that you have the choice. The difficulty is to identify the pattern which keeps your energy levels low. The challenge is to mark out the options. Once you know them, you can then choose the option with the higher level of energy."

Clara looked at him contemplatively. "It sounds easy," she then said.

"It is easy. Still, most people choose to stay on the lower energy levels. When you serve Ma'at, as I do, you will always know which decision to make. She is the one who balances out your nine spiritual bodies of the Light—one of which is your AB, your heart body. She is the one holding the keys to the open, pure heart. Call on her. She will always let you know immediately what the path of your heart is. You will immediately notice an uplifiting in your energy levels."

"How many Neters are in the Egyptian pantheon?" Clara asked after a while.

"It varies," Anubis answered, absorbed in his thoughts.

Then he straightened himself. "It is not important, Clara. I will introduce them to you when the time has come. You will get acquainted with their energy. They are mighty beings. They can be quite breathtaking. They represent all spectrums of colors, vibrations, forms, the nothingness, and all sounds as well as the silence."

He looked pensive. "They mirror to you everything you have hidden in your darkest corner of your being. It takes strength, stamina, and power for each and every human being to stay aware and hold the space within themselves for all those divine and diverse beings and vibrations!"

Clara stared at him with a troubled expression on her face. "This sounds as if it might be quite overpowering."

Anubis nodded. "Mankind preferred a one-god policy later, for good reason. However, this had far-reaching consequences for humanity. In confining selected qualities to only one being, a dangerous narrowing of the definition or understanding of the divine took place."

He sighed. "It had seemed easier to deal with an authoritarian old Father-God than with all those colorful emanations of the divine. The price you pay is high, however. You separate yourself from the experience of other divine vibrations. Furthermore, and above all, you separated yourself from all feminine Christ consciousness. Yes, there were and there are many women reaching Christ consciousness. It is tragic that mankind, which absorbed womankind and nihilated it, gradually lost the feeling for the sacredness of the feminine. There is no balance of the masculine and the feminine qualities here on this earth. In fact, what is needed is true union of the masculine and feminine in each and every one of you."

Clara stared at him. "Erna would be really interested to hear that," she mumbled.

Anubis ignored her comment. "In order for the human race to survive on this planet, you must re-establish the balance between the masculine and the feminine. You must begin to care for the planet instead of only exploiting it. You must develop a maternal, as well as paternal, compassion for all living beings on this earth. If you continue exploiting the planet like this, your race will be erased."

His face twisted with pain.

6

THE POWER OF DREAMING

"How can I imagine the masculine and the feminine as one?" Clara asked. She sat on the only chair in her kitchen and watched him pour a bottle of ouzo into a glass. She had been quite stunned when he had pointed at the bottle high up on her kitchen shelf.

"Can I get one of those? I do have fond memories of Greece," he had added in a casual tone. "We might be going there soon. Do you want a glass as well?"

"No, thank you," she said, too bewildered to pick up that line of the conversation.

She repeated her question. "Anubis, please tell me about the masculine and the feminine and how they could possible become one. I do not understand."

The ice cubes made a metallic noise when he dropped them into the glass. The clear ouzo turned into a milky liquid.

Anubis looked at her thoughtfully.

"There are no role models," Clara murmured. "At least not for the women. I do not know of any enlightened or realized woman, neither of today nor of the past."

"And yet, there are many," Anubis said in a humble tone. "Have you ever heard of Chenrezig and Yeshe Shogyal?"

Clara shook her head.

"Chenrezig was a much revered wise man in Tibet," Anubis said. "When he was close to reaching enlightenment, he realized he needed a female counterpart, an equally wise and enlightened being, to reach the next step of enlightenment. Unfortunately, there was no woman incarnated at the time in Tibet who would be equal to him, so he went into meditation and called upon the Goddess Saraswati to help him. Saraswati decided to incarnate as a woman, and Chenrezig waited until she, as Yeshe Shogyal, became a young woman. He then went in a deep tantric trance state with her, and they both reached enlightenment for the sake and the blessing of all people from that time until now."

"So he needed her to reach the next step?" Clara asked.

Anubis nodded. "Yes, he needed a female counterpart to strengthen his lightbody and fill his physical body with ethereal light. The tantric way is one way to achieve this. The Egyptians knew that."

"What do you mean with *until now*? Are they still alive?" Clara asked.

Anubis only smiled. "Close your eyes," he said.

Clara did as he requested.

Anubis lowered his voice to a whisper. "Imagine Yeshe Shogyal in your heart. Imagine her as the manifestation of the highest feminine qualities you can think of. Tune into them, as if they were real."

At first nothing happened. Clara easily visualized a small feminine figure in her heart, but the figure seemed to freeze when Clara attempted to tune into her energy. Suddenly, a very sweet and delicate vibration made itself known, like the faint fragrance of an exquisite flower. It was so delicate that Clara instinctively stopped breathing—as if she was afraid her breath would chase off that soft energy. She was reminded of a white lily blossom slowly opening and giving herself away to the sun. The opening seemed very slow and endless.

Clara felt ravished. "This is so beautiful," she whispered.

"Yes," Anubis said. "I can feel that you are connected with her vibration. Now, slowly let go of Yeshe Shoguyal's energy and imagine Chenrezig as the highest enlightened masculine presence in your heart."

This time, Clara did not have any problems with perceiving the masculine vibration. It was instantly there, within a second. His presence proved powerful, and he seemed to be everywhere. Although his presence was unwavering, it was not intimidating in any respect.

"He does not have a beginning or end," Clara whispered in awe. "He seems everywhere—inside me as well as outside."

"Yes. He is a pure and enlightened presence holding the space. Indeed, holding all spaces within and outside. Revel in this vibration, Clara. It is of utmost exquisiteness, like the one of Yeshe Shogyal."

His strong, masculine presence seemed to unflinchingly stretch and expand into the farthest corners of her body. It was moving and utterly still at the same time. Her body started to tingle, and she heaved a long sigh.

There is a part in me which wants to totally yield to this energy, she thought incredulously.

"You see," Anubis said quietly, "polarities are already starting to build up. You, as a woman, are opening to his presence. Your body begins to surrender and let go of tension."

He laughed softly. "Continue to enjoy this while tuning into Yeshe, too. Imagine them both in the tantric yoga posture with her sitting on his lap, her legs around his waist. See how they slowly merge their energy bodies."

When Clara visualized those two figures together in her heart, she immediately felt a rush of a sweet and powerful energy moving through her body.

She had the impression that Yeshe's vibrations of love and surrender were expanding in the vibratory field of Chenrezig's presence while his capability of staying present and worshipping her deepened at the same pace. Those two amazing beings strengthened each other's vibrations beyond anything she could have ever imagined. She felt it in her heart as it radiated out into her whole body.

How amazing this is, she thought breathlessly. The bringing together of those two energies creates pure bliss. No way could I make this up! It feels too real.

When she continued visualizing the merging of Yeshe and Chenrezig, she felt them truly becoming one spinning, unified field of energy. It emitted tiny sparkles of light. Clara was stunned.

"Can you see how they metabolize light?" Anubis asked quietly.

Clara only nodded. She was so grateful to be allowed to witness their union. It is a sacred dance of the masculine and feminine energies, she caught herself thinking. She was witnessing it and at the same time she could feel herself being deeply moved by it.

"The light they are emitting is a blessing for all beings throughout all times," Anubis explained in a low voice. "You perceive yourself as part of the light when you tune into those two enlightened beings. You strengthen your own lightbody, your *KA* body, as we call it, with this tuning in. You serve the world with this, Clara, and it is all a matter of dreaming intent, holding the image in your heart, and resting in the love and presence of the two."

He paused for a moment. "When love and presence merge, both energies begin to deepen and expand. This is the tantric secret of the union of the masculine and the feminine. In these times, this is so urgently needed: human beings connecting with their higher selves

116

and dreaming the true union of man and woman."

* * *

"So, what was your topic last time?" Erna asked.

"We talked about the masculine and the feminine," Clara answered absentmindedly. She opened the fridge. Didn't she have any butter for the croissant Erna had brought her?

"Pardon?" Erna asked wide-eyed. "The masculine and the feminine? For heaven's sake, what is there to *talk* about?"

Clara laughed. Then she closed the door of the fridge with a swoosh. "It is complicated," she said gravely.

"I bet," Erna muttered and rolled her eyes. "Please, spare me the details."

"I will," Clara said, grinning. "It is too difficult, anyway, to summarize it in a few sentences. It is a long story, as long as the rift between men and women. We would need to go way back—back to those times before the split occurred."

"Before the split?" Erna's eyebrows raised. "You want to tell me there was once a time when . . ."

"Well, apparently so," Clara said evasively. She suddenly felt very tired.

"You mean, we were once androgynous, like those tiny animals—what are they called?—*mollusca*? Those jellyfish types of animals?" Erna asked incredulously.

Clara nodded. She let herself drop onto her kitchen chair. Stretching her arms and caressing them gently along the sides, she said slowly, "And you know what? It seems that it is all about becoming whole again. The masculine and the feminine in one's own body. *Animus* and *Anima* reintegrated."

Erna shook her head in disbelief. "No way," she said. "How

should this work? And besides, where would all the fun be? Come on, Clara, how boring does this sound?"

Clara looked at her. "Do you think it is boring with me?" she then asked provocatively and knocked her knuckles on the table. "We do not feel the sexual urge to copulate, and still we enjoy ourselves together somewhat, don't we?"

"We enjoy ourselves *somewhat*?" Erna echoed her words, pouting her lips. "Are you serious?"

Clara beamed. Her tiredness had disappeared all of a sudden, and she had become quite cheery.

"Just fishing for compliments," she said airily and patted one of Erna's hands. "Please, my dear one, laugh!"

Erna only let out a muffled sound.

Clara turned serious again. "Imagine yourself as an enlightened being," she then said with a stern voice.

Erna moaned.

"Come on, Erna," Clara said. "We both know that you are not, but let us just pretend for a moment you are! Okay?"

Erna moaned even louder. Then she flashed her teeth. "Okay," she said and closed her eyes. "This is me," she said in a comical voice. "Enlightened!" Then she turned silent.

Clara also closed her eyes. She imagined white-golden light trickling into her head. It filled her head completely, then it slowly flowed down her throat and into her arms, her upper and lower body, then into her legs and feet, and from there, it flowed into the earth. All of a sudden, she sensed a shift in the atmosphere around her. It was as if a more profound reality had moved in, a new vibration with a deeper truth to it.

"This is it," she said quietly. "Now imagine your enlightened Anima in the form of a woman and your enlightened Animus in the form of a man, side by side in your heart."

"Got them," Erna said after quite some time. "The man was difficult to imagine," she murmured.

Erna moaned. "It feels pretty good," she admitted and opened her eyes to slits. "It actually feels pretty damn good."

"Great," Clara said. "Now imagine yourself moving into your feminine enlightened part and standing vis-à-vis that masculine part of yours, which is also enlightened. Can you see him? Can you feel his presence?"

"Wow!" Erna said after a while. "He is radiant! What an amazing being he is now. I am completely ravished by this guy. I could immediately lie down with him. I can even feel it in my body!"

She turned mute for a moment.

"This is so amazing, Clara. Is he real?"

Erna opened her eyes.

"How can this be?" she asked. "I mean, how can I experience him so clearly, although he is just an image in my imagination. Why do I react to him so strongly, Clara? This is the most amazing thing I have ever experienced."

"There is much to explore here," Clara said, nodding. "Anubis told me that shamans speak of the spirit mate. He or she is your equal counterpart within you. There is even a sacred marriage ceremony you could go through. It is the marriage of the masculine and the feminine within you. It is a marriage of self to self."

"Does this mean I do not have any other partner in this world?" Erna asked.

"No, not all," Clara said. "It means you are one within yourself, and you do not need to look for another being to feel whole. When you are with someone in the physical, and if he is committed to his inner woman as you are to your inner man, your way of being together is entirely different. It is based on free choice rather than on co-dependency. There is no leaning into each other, no merging of circles of power, no domination or subordination. When you consciously live with your spirit mate, you will also magnetise very different people in your life. This is what Anubis said."

"A man committed to his inner woman!" Erna repeated with awe in her voice. "How could I possibly imagine this to be?"

Clara smiled and bit into one of the apples on the table. "Anubis once pointed out to me a man who had gone through the self-to-self marriage," she said, chewing on the apple. "When I spoke to this man, I could feel his gentleness, how sensitive and receptive, how utterly caring he was. But he was also a man, you know? He did not leave his circle of power. He was fully present in all his gentleness, like a sword stuck straight into the earth. His presence was like electricity filling the room. At the same time, I felt as if he would be carrying me on his arms. But he was not. It had nothing to do with me. He was carrying his inner woman, praising her, worshipping her. And she totally surrendered to him. You could see that he knew. He knew, in the depth of his heart, that she belonged to him. His inner woman surrendered to him, because he took care of her. Which means he was committed to staying fully present with her whatever she did. He would not abandon her. He was there, ready to merge with her in every moment."

Clara took another bite. "Anubis told me that this is the secret formula about becoming whole: worshipping the feminine and surrendering to the masculine—all within oneself. Amazing, isn't it?"

"Yes," Erna said, visibly impressed. "And then? Is this the end of the story?"

Clara shook her head. "I guess not. Once you have opened up to this, the real exploration starts, because you want to know the other and all his or her facets. You learn from each other. You truly learn how to love the other half. The magic is that whatever you learn together is automatically manifested in the physical. This is what Anubis told me. As within, so without. There is no difference. There is not even a time difference between your inner experience and the outer manifestations."

She sat down on the chair.

"When we consciously enjoy oneness with our inner mate, we have the same vibration on the outside. This is why we then draw other, more balanced people into our lives. And we motivate other people to seek balance with their inner mates so that they, too, become whole."

Clara sighed. "I am only at the very beginning of this, Erna. You know well how much I am fighting with my relationships. I want to change my partner, change myself, give it up, hang onto my hope, resist any change, anything, you name it. Now I feel there is much potential in this exploration of the masculine and feminine within me. So much potential. I am desperate to explore it."

"Me too," Erna said, nodding heavily. "I want to meet my inner man again, you bet!"

* * *

"I do not expect you would want to reveal yourself to Marco?" Clara said solemnly, the next time she met Anubis at the lake.

"For sure, I will," he answered. "When the time has come." He smiled. "Maybe next week. Maybe in a few aeons. I have no idea."

"You are joking," Clara said, slightly annoyed.

"Also," she said and smiled sheepishly, "should you not know? You are some sort of a god, after all!" Her nostrils flared.

"Tell me," she said teasingly, "what is the point of me hanging around with a god when he does not even know the future?"

Anubis's smile deepened. "There is a golden rule," he then said with a sepulchral voice. "A golden rule for all beings of the light, and it would be damn good . . ." he made a theatrical pause, "if it were also a fundamental guiding principle for the human race."

"What is it?" Clara asked impetuously.

"All Beings of Light must respect the freewill of others. We do not allow ourselves to step over into other beings' circles of power. It includes the right for free choice. Sometimes the circle of power is well defended, sometimes it is virtually not there, as it is underneath another circle of power that is lying on it, like a gravestone."

"What a horrible metaphor."

Clara shuddered.

Anubis shook his head. "You should know, this is always in agreement with everybody involved. If you are in victim mode, you agree that there is someone or something dominating you. You are then easily being overstepped by another force. If you are aware of your circle of power, you better make sure you stay the master or mistress of it."

He smiled. "It is one of the most challenging and difficult things for all of us to not step into another's circle of power—to not become intrusive. All Beings of Light respect this universal law. So, to make a long story short, I have no idea when we are going to meet all together; me, you, and your partner, my love."

"I really do hope it will take place soon," Clara said.

"Do not worry," Anubis said slowly. "He knows of me already."

"How does he know?" she said, astonished.

"I am part of you, my love. He feels me, feels my vibration within you. He might not experience it consciously. It should only be a matter of time until we will all meet in person. Unless he is so afraid that he decides to stop having contact with you. I doubt, however, that this will happen. You have become more magnetic—and also more scary—for him during this process."

* * *

"He is going to meet Marco and not me?" Erna stomped her foot. "You are not serious, Clara. Are you?"

Clara waved her hands. "Calm down." She offered Erna a faint smile. "I have not yet asked him about you. So will you please . . . "

"After all I have done for you?" Erna said, raising her arms high up. "I have searched the Internet days and nights for information on this guy! I have had endless discussions with you on spiritual union versus a good one-night stand. Ah, what a friend you are!"

She threw her hands and arms up in the air in a comical display.

"You will make up for this, my friend. I will not let you go easily with this."

"Erna, could you please cool down?" Clara dropped onto her sofa. "It might take aeons! Did you hear me? Aeons! Or even worse—we might both be grandmothers with lavender hair and half deaf with no aspiration whatsoever anymore to discuss gender-related issues." She pushed a cushion aside.

"There is nothing I can do about it, Erna. Anubis talked about the 'freewill' of everybody. I need to accept this, but . . . "

"But?" Erna asked, hope rising in her voice.

"But I can ask him . . ." Clara's voice trailed off.

"Ask him what?" Erna said rebelliously.

"Ask him whether he would be willing to meet this sweet little bitch of a friend of mine."

"Yes!" Erna beamed and curled her hands into fists. "Tell him how important I am for you! Tell him how so very interested I am in all that tantric stuff. As a matter of fact, I even talked to Adrian about it the other day."

"You mean the guy from the fitness center?" Clara asked, her eyebrows raised.

"Yes! He said that he would be very open to those things. I

mean, really! He does not pretend. I can feel it!"

Clara grinned. "So open," she echoed her friend's words with an ironic undertone. "I mean, really, Erna! The only thing this guy wants is probably a good . . . "

"Wait!" Erna raised her hand in a defensive stopping movement. "Do not continue! You are judging! You have prejudices, Clara. That is not fair. You better get rid of them as soon as possible; otherwise, you are never going to get even close to enlightenment! Isn't that one of those forty-two Rules of Ma'at we read about yesterday?"

Erna wrestled with a piece of paper which she had stuffed in one of her back pockets of her jeans. "Where is it?" she murmured, hectically gliding her forefinger across the paper. "Here is the killing, the sabotage, the greediness, the cursing . . . ah, here we go."

Then she loudly exclaimed, "Hail, Tenemiu, I have not slandered nor put anyone down. I have not judged." She threw a menacing look towards Clara.

"You see! There you are, Clara! Did you hear? No judgments; otherwise, no entry into the Egyptian heavens. I mean, you do not even know this man of mine!"

"Interesting rule, this," Clara murmured. "How would the world be if that were one of the ten holy commandments." She sighed, and a faint smile played at her lips. "Right you are, Erna. I am sorry. No, I do not know this guy, and yes, I cannot rule out the possibility of him being genuinely interested in the spiritual dimension of sex."

Clara tried to keep a straight face as she tapped on a sofa cushion. "Sit down," she said in a reconciling tone. "Let me know what happened between the two of you. I am really curious! You have kept very quiet lately about your affair with him."

She could read in Erna's face that Erna was struggling between still feeling indignant or already appeased.

"I am going to get us a drink," Erna said majestically and

scuffled to the kitchen. "Then we will see! I might then be willing to talk!"

* * *

"If you dream a world full of love, there will be a world full of love," Anubis said.

"This is ridiculous!" Clara's dismay was evident in her voice.

"I won't believe that esoteric flower-power-on-which-cloud-are-we-flying-today rubbish. He is a jerk, that's what he is."

She panted as she climbed up the stairs to her apartment. Just a few minutes ago, she'd had an unpleasant encounter with the landlord, an encounter she would rather not have had. He had been chasing her again for leaving the main door of the building unlocked in the evening. She could not convince him that it had not been her fault. For some reason, he thought she would be the only one returning home late in the night. In vain, she had tried to convince him of the opposite.

"You are the youngest here in this house!" he snapped back. "You will not tell me that eighty-year-old Mrs. Gempke returns home as late as one in the morning!"

She had only been able to get rid of him after promising him to take more care. Now she felt pretty stupid. She had admitted to a crime she had not committed. This is how far one goes to avoid further confrontations with jerks, she had thought grimly.

"I do not expect you to believe me," Anubis had said seriously. He had suddenly appeared at her side, choreographically stepping up the stairs with her. He was quite a sight with his white and golden clothes. For a split second, his face changed into the mask of a dark jackal.

Clara held her breath.

"You must explore and find out for yourself," he added.

"How?" Clara trembled, still taken aback by the powerful appearance.

"How did you feel yesterday?"

"I felt awful." She inserted the key into the lock of her apartment door. "I felt lonely and isolated. As if nobody loved me, and there was no purpose in my life."

"And did you believe in your story?"

She shook her head. "I got pissed off by it," she said now, smiling lightly. Entering the corridor of her apartment, she dropped her bags to the floor and went through to her living room. "I must admit, it took me some time to figure out that I do not want to believe in it. Then my mood quickly changed."

"You changed the picture in the mirror." Anubis nodded. He had followed her and now sat on her sofa, his legs crossed. His eyes screened the environment in a casual and non-intrusive way. His manner was graceful, as usual, and reflected utmost serenity.

I love that he is so calm and composed, Clara thought. He seems so centered and grounded in himself, as if all threads of the world would lead right into his heart, where he would gather them and lay them out anew and caress them with incredible tenderness and integrity.

She revelled at his sight.

"Don't you want to sit down, my love?" He had obviously noticed her reverence for him.

She blushed. "I am going to get some water first."

When she came back from the kitchen, she asked, "What do you mean, I changed the picture?"

"You decided to not believe in the picture that your mirror showed to you at that very moment," Anubis said. "There is no way the mirror can uphold the picture if you do not believe in it anymore. It will only show what you believe. The more you believe in your dreams, the more your mirrors will show you those dreams. They are absolutely one-hundred-percent true. Some beliefs are so strong that it takes much powerful dreaming to create another picture—or another reality."

His voice became more urgent. "You are all dreamers with tremendous power to manifest your dreams. It is a power beyond your imagination, and it calls for much more respect than you currently have. Don't underestimate it, Clara. Don't disrespect it."

"I could never talk to anybody about my experience with you apart from Erna," Clara muttered. "I would be called a maniac, or a lunatic, or even worse."

There was silence in the room.

Then Anubis said, "It is lunatic to kill each other like you humans do. Your whole world is distorted, and you believe in what your radio and TV shows present you as real. You have no idea what is real and what is not. The human race is so confused."

"So, how could we possibly end the confusion?" Clara asked.

"You need to always return to your awareness of what you are in the deep. You are consciousness rippled out in form. Your form, and indeed your entire life, will change according to the level of your own awareness of being pure consciousness, which is in fact, as you have already noticed yourself, my love, pure love. In the center of your cells is pure bliss—you remember this quote, don't you?"

She only nodded.

"It is true, and the more you know it and dream it and imagine it and set your intent around it to actually experience it, the more it will become your reality. It is a synchronistic world, meaning thoughts become your reality the very instant you are dreaming it. The mirror cannot show anything other than what you are prepared to see. So don't hesitate to dream, my love. It is your gateway to the heavens. Start right away—and take your landlord as an exercise. It is a good exercise, and he is a good man. It is not that he is not worth it!"

When he saw Clara's incredulous face, he started laughing. Then he opened his arms.

"Please come to me, my love," he said tenderly. "Let us dream. Let us create a uniform field of love together. Dreaming is one of the most uplifting and empowering experiences you can grant yourself. Let's get started."

* * *

Clara drifted in and out of strange dreams, dreams of being touched, of the sensation of warm skin moving along her half-naked body. At some point she became acutely aware of her bedcover touching her skin. It gave her a sense of nesting, of being held and being protected. Wherever her body came in contact with the silken material, her pores seemed to open up to its smooth softness, and she relaxed deeper into its intimacy. At times, her body felt unusually heavy, and she was aware of its weight pressing into the mattress. The next moment, she seemed to have lost the feeling of its weight altogether and experienced herself more as hovering somewhere out there. It was as if her awareness was ebbing and flowing into and out of her body. She let herself be immersed by all those sensations.

After a while, she became aware of a tingling in her vagina. It had been there all the time, and it actually shifted her out of the dreamtime and awakened her. There was an uncertainty within her whether she would decide to fully wake up or stay in this strange dreaming state. When she focused on the tingling, it became much stronger. It was as if her focusing energized her lower body and, in particular, the skin and the warm and soft flesh around her clitoris. It was extremely powerful and sweet. It was as if she were massaging her clitoris with her awareness. It did not feel like a normal massage, as her skin was not being touched. It was more like a velvety sensation pervading her body through and through. Her clitoris seemed to be a three-dimensional space pulsing softly in ecstasy. She had not done anything. She had not touched herself. She had not even moved. It was amazing.

Suddenly, she heard his voice in her head. *Your body is currently being penetrated by the light of your consciousness. Do you notice this, my love?*

I do, she responded in her thoughts. Again she felt herself shifting between a state of sleepiness and a state of utter vigilance. "My body reacts to my conscious focusing," she murmured. "I cannot believe this."

As if to make sure that she was not dreaming, she slipped her fingers underneath the duvet. When she touched herself, she knew instantly that the touch was in no way as intense as the sensation of her consciousness penetrating the flesh of her vagina. Her hand felt heavy and insensitive. She moved her fingers away. Again, she concentrated on the three-dimensional space around her clitoris. She imagined the space in and between the cells of her body being touched and flooded by light. Instantly, the ecstatic vibration was there again. Or was it that she just connected with it?

It had probably been there all the time, she thought. I was so distracted by the physical sensation of my fingers that I had not noticed it.

"This is one of the secrets of tantra," she heard his calm voice saying inside her mind. "It is the merging of your enlightened energy body with your physical body. It happens all the time, again and again, in waves and other formations. The energy body energizes the physical body. It can be your own, or it can be another person's energy body. In the case of Osiris, it was Isis. Her energy body was so strong that when she merged her energy body with Osiris' physical body, she brought him back into life. This is the true meaning of the Isis/Osiris legend. There is another famous couple who had been on that same sacred path."

"Who were they?" Clara asked telepathically.

"Joshua and Mary Magdalene."

She shook her head in disbelief.

"Don't get hooked up by stories, he said calmly. Sense the energy within yourself and acknowledge the truth with your body mind. You will realize that you exist in different bodies or dimensions at the same time."

"Why do I not experience this amazing swaying more often?" Clara asked.

"It needs practice. You need to be aware of your energy body and your physical body at the same time."

He grew quiet inside her mind for a moment, then he said reassuringly, "the shift will occur gradually, and you will be more and more able to sense the two bodies within yourself. You will learn how to consciously steer the energy by your own pure focusing. Your dreambody has already grown so strong that you can experience it while being awake."

"I am awake?" Clara asked.

"Yes, my love, you are more awake than ever, because you can experience both the physical aspects of living on this earth as well as your energy body movements. Since your energy body is full of light and fills up your physical body, you will become aware how the two, indeed, live their oneness."

Clara felt him leaving her. "Please stay with me," she begged.

"I am always with you. In the higher dimension where I dwell, I am one with you, Clara. Stay aware of the other dimensions, and you will know that separation does not exist. There is no way you can separate light from light."

* * *

"It sounds as if you were aware of your physical body and your KA body at the same time," Erna contemplated.

Clara had told her about her amazing experience, adding that she could not recall any other sexual intercourse with a touch as exquisite as this.

"You never know the future, though . . ." Erna had briefly interrupted her. "We will not give up our dreams and visions, will we?"

"What have you read about the KA body?" Clara retorted.

"As far as I understand, KA is a web of interwoven strands of light that permeates the body continuously."

Erna looked towards the pile of books dangerously leaning against the wall. She jumped up, crossed the room, and pulled one book out of the pile. "This should be it," she exclaimed, scanning the content page.

"Ah, yes. Here we go. KA is your holographic double made of light. It is the interface with the Earth web. It holds past life memories, can trigger deep healings, and is the connection to your soul. Your divine KA acts as an interface for the soul to be brought into the physical realms."

Then she groaned. "Listen to this," she said. "To realize and embody your divine KA requires that you also look deep into your shadow and its faces and forms."

"Shhh. . . ." She grinned and closed the book with a dull bang. "Seems as if there is no shortcut to enlightenment. We need to go into those underworlds you and Anubis are talking about." She smiled sheepishly. "I thought I could skip that part."

Clara started to chuckle.

"I would love to calm you down, my friend, by comforting you by saying there are no shadows in you. Alas, my dear friend, I am sorry to say I do see plenty, and the challenges will be manifold."

Erna looked at her as if she wanted to jump at her.

Then she started to grin.

"Never mind," she said. "There will be some fun along this

sacred path. Otherwise, you will not find me there."

"Remember the promises," Clara said priestly. "That *one blazing ball of light* you once talked about! Remember?"

Erna ignored her comment and peeped into the book again.

"That should interest you too," she said. "The divine KA is an aspect of God, or a God form. In Egypt, this was seen as one of the Neters. Your divine KA could be Isis or Anubis, for example. Similarly, in Tibetan Buddhism and Hinduism, this is a visualized deity—Buddha, god, or goddess form—which you learn to merge with over time through meditation practices." She looked at Clara with wide eyes. "Now we know what you are up to," she exclaimed cheerfully. "For some reason, you chose Anubis to merge with and strengthen this lightbody of yours."

Clara looked at her with a blank face. Then she stretched her hands. "It is pretty real, this merging with him," she concluded.

"Sounds like it," Erna remarked soulfully.

7

TEACHINGS

He materialized into the air wearing a short black skirt, a white T-shirt, and sandals of fine brown leather. He bowed down to her, then briskly walked across the room and sat down on her sofa.

She revelled at the sight of him. He had the air of a mighty king, serene and serious, but there was also the fleeting impression of light flickering and dancing around him, as if to tease him or her.

"Let us start the lessons," he said in a matter-of-fact tone, his smile betraying the seriousness in his voice. "Time to get to the bones of things, my love."

"To the bones of things," she echoed. "What do you mean by that?"

"To the bones of things," he repeated. "To the vast void within the material world."

"I do not understand," she said.

"Yes, you do," he said slowly, looking intensely into her eyes.

There was a stirring in her forehead. Her attention was drawn to her head. Then she had the sensation of something locking in place, like a key being turned in a hole and then snapping into place.

"That feels very peaceful!" she murmured.

A question turned up in her mind. For a split second, she moved her eyes away. The moment of peace was gone, interrupted by the sudden movement of her eyes.

How annoying, she thought, dispirited. Where was this wonderful place she had just been? She started screening her head. She could not find it. Where had she just been?

"Is it not amazing," she heard him saying, "how fast one drops into this place and falls out of it again?"

She nodded reluctantly.

"Do not worry," he said. "This place is within you. You will find it again."

His reassuring voice calmed her down. She still felt, however, as if a radar light was inside her head, searching unflinchingly for that place.

"Don't force it," he said. "You will remember the connections you made in your brain. Have patience and relax. Chances are higher that you will get there again when you are in a relaxed and receptive state."

She shook her head defiantly. "I want to be there now!" she said impetuously.

He laughed. "You really want to know."

Anubis fell silent again. After a while, he said with a quiet voice in her mind, "look into my eyes again, and stay with them."

She looked up, envisioning his face. His black and slightly enlarged pupils drew her into him. She followed the call. Suddenly she felt this click again in her head. There. There it was.

Her gaze turned inward. At the same time, she did not stop looking into his eyes. Her breath became shallow. Something in her head opened up. She had the image of a giant cave revealing itself inside her head. Then the cave seemed to be mirrored deep down in her womb. A space had opened up there too, a space which was equally expanding along with the space in her head.

"Hold those two spaces," she heard Anubis whisper from afar. "Focus on them, and do not let them escape your attention."

Whilst she did, she could feel something in her soar and move out of her head. It spiraled into the air and disappeared into the void.

"That was a release of some old stuff," Anubis mumbled. "No need to know what it was. It did not serve you any longer, and so it left. Sometimes it is *that* easy."

Clara had no idea what he was talking about. She did not want to interrupt the connection, though, and forced herself to suppress any questions. She focused on those two expanding caves; the one in her body and the one in his eyes. The sensation was bizarre, as she seemed to be hovering in the center of those caves while being hooked up by his steady and reassuring gaze.

Then there was a new sensation.

Clara felt like she was saying backwards and forwards, moving along an invisible figure eight that stretched out between herself and Anubis. She first noticed the swaying in her womb area, then it gradually expanded up and down her body. It was as if her body was dancing in multiple figure eights. They were very joyful, those movements, and after a short while, Clara became quite warm.

"This is the dance of the chakras," Anubis said. "We are dancing together in all thirteen chakras. The heat you are noticing is sekhem, or life force, in your energy body. It is being stirred up in your lightbody and spilling over into your physical body."

"Thirteen chakras?" she asked incredulously.

"Well, actually, many more than just thirteen." He smiled. "But thirteen should be enough for a start, don't you think?"

"Why are your eyes so important?" she whispered.

"When you enter the void, it is good to have an anchor. You explore the void while being held by my eyes. When you rest your eyes in mine, you know that you will not lose yourself in the void. Feeling one's own dissolution is quite frightening. It might actually prevent you from entering higher states of awareness."

"I see," Clara said, dumbfounded.

"With some practice, you will be able to stay conscious while we are surfing the unknown."

Anubis's face lit up and his eyes seemed to smile. "Then the real adventure begins."

"What do you mean by that?" Clara sat up, alert.

"I will be holding the space so that you can say hello to all your demons," Anubis said lightheartedly. "Say hello, and kiss them goodbye, so to say."

Clara stared at him.

"I am joking," he said soothingly. "Those figures of eights stir up much energy in your Djed pillar of the spine. The spine is the location where your unresolved issues dwell. As long as there are still knots and stresses along the spine, you are limited in bringing light into your physical body."

He smiled reassuringly. "Do not worry, Clara. Nothing will take place that you have not wholeheartedly called forward. You decided to walk this path long ago, and now the doors are open. There are quite a few of us here to support you—and others—on this way towards awakening to your true nature. Trust me. Not without reason do they call me the way-shower. I will always be here and accompany you on your path."

* * *

"Does he also talk about ecstasy?" Erna asked, eagerness lighting her eyes.

Clara rolled her eyes. "What exactly would you like to know?" Then she started grinning.

"Well, what is all this about the kundalini energy? You know what, can you ask him next time? I am desperate to know." Erna groaned.

"I know." Clara laughed. "I am not sure that you would like his response, though."

"Why should I not?" Erna asked with indignation in her voice. "You know you are not the only one here who is evolving."

Clara patted her on her shoulders.

"Calm down, my sister," she said soothingly, though she kept a smile on her face. "It is just that he seems to be more interested in transformation of the physical than hot sex. I assume he might even like to equate his teachings with the end of projections. You know how we all like to project our desires onto other people. We hope they could fulfill all our longings. We can get pretty passionate about this."

"Oooooh," Erna said with much regret in her voice. Then her face brightened again. "I cannot imagine that the end of projections might equate to the end of passion. Please, Clara, ask him next time, will you?"

Clara eyed her closely. Then she shook her head.

"I cannot promise anything. You know those conversations do not take place when the mind is in control."

"I imagine." Erna sighed. "It is letting go while keeping up the intent at the same time. The usual *koan*—the 'clapping with one hand' stuff. My stunning goddess, sometimes I wonder why all those secrets are not being revealed to us in an easier way."

"We would not understand them, I guess," Clara said. "Look around and see how beautiful this planet is. There is abundance everywhere. It is breathtaking. However, we are all running on scarcity mode. We rush through the world, from birth to death, and we ignore the most obvious facts. I guess this is why there is a mythical layer around the truths of the world. We are asked to move into them holographically rather than crash into them horizontally."

Erna gaped at Clara. "Wow," she exclaimed. "What an insight."

Clara smiled. "I have no idea where those words came from. Somewhere within us, those truths are buried, and when we sniff them, they come out like a micro-tornado. Come on, let's go and get something decent to eat. I am hungry."

She stood, grabbed Erna's hands, and made her get up from the couch.

* * *

"Hello, my love. What are you pondering about?" he asked softly.

She sighed. "Too much going on in my head," she said.

"How is the weather?"

"The weather?" she repeated, puzzled. "Are you joking? Why should I talk about the weather? You see how it is!"

They stood on Clara's terrace, watching big white clouds occasionally drift across the sun as it sank into the horizon.

"Come on," Anubis said. "There is more behind the weather talk. You should know, my beloved shamaness."

"Yes, I guess so," she admitted after a moment.

Clara realized how her cheeks were getting warm. She cleared her throat and closed her eyes. Then she started to whisper. "Autumn winds are coming, crazy winds containing voluptuous devils of dust. There is a bright stripe of blue stretching along the horizon with clear-cut shapes of the high mountains far away. I love that kind of weather. The wind is still warm and full of fierceful passions and promises. It reminds me . . ." She stopped talking and more heat rushed into her face.

"What does the wind remind you of?" he asked tenderly.

She hesitated.

A smile flitted across his face. "I am the guide into the underworlds, Clara. There is nothing to be embarrassed about. Everything has its right of existence. Just say it. What does the wind remind you of?"

"I was lying on my sofa this morning, moving in and out of sleep. Suddenly there was this enormous energy bubble coming up my root chakra. I orgasmed, just simply lying there, half asleep. I could not believe it. It was quite joyful." She fell silent, sweeping her hands down her face as if to cover it up.

"That was all?" he asked, amused.

"Well, yes," she answered hesitantly. "Isn't that enough?"

"Those states of bliss will increase," he said calmly. "The more knots in your energy body that dissolve, the more you will experience the free flow of energy, or sekhem, within you. I am not surprised. You have done a lot of releasing recently."

Clara looked up and stared at him questionly.

"Is this what trauma healing is about?" she asked.

"Of course," he answered. "Whenever there is a trauma locked somewhere within your body, the energy slows down. It is like a big stone in a river. The water is being retarded and forced to divert. Once the stone is removed, the water can flow unhindered."

Anubis put his arms around Clara. "This is the way to let bliss surge into your body, my love. Bliss will change your brain patterns. You will increasingly experience higher and higher frequencies within yourself, both in your physical body as well as emotionally and spiritually."

He looked away for a moment. The sun dropped behind the horizon in a dramatic crescendo of streaks of red, orange, and black. Immediately, the temperature dropped and Clara began to shiver. Soon it would be dark.

"It takes courage," Anubis said slowly. "When the light hits the dark, there might be pain beyond words. It is through the release of the pain that the light can enter. You will know when you have gone all the way. It feels whole. There will be more and more more states of bliss. This is my promise to everyone who is committed to walk this path."

* * *

Clara stirred the milk into the hot, black liquid. The voices around her were earsplitting, and she already regretted leaving her apartment for a brief break to go around the corner to her favorite coffee shop. Her thoughts circulated around a remark from a shaman teacher she had met at a conference recently. He was a trauma-healing teacher, and she had been listening to his introductory lecture. When he finished his talk, he looked around and asked who would like to experience his method. There was no response. Impulsively, he motioned Clara and another woman to get up and sit together, right in the center of the circle of people. She had hesitated but then obeyed his calling, noticing how much her body had tensed when he picked her out of the crowd.

"Ready to order?" she heard the waiter asking.

She looked up. "No, thank you." She blinked rapidly, surprised to see the menu still lying open in front of her. "Maybe later." She smiled apologetically and closed the menu.

She took a sip of her coffee. What the hell did the teacher mean when he said, "You do not seem to be part of this group." His remark had deeply upset her. Everybody had stared at her and this other woman. She felt terrorized and ashamed at the same time. Her mind had raced. Had she done anything wrong? Did the others think that she perceived herself as being different, or even superior? She had been rigid with fear. Why was it so very dangerous for her to not be part of the group?

The whole exercise left her desperately stranded. Even her dancing around an imaginary fire as an Indian tribe member on the mesa in the American deserts, which the teacher had initiated afterwards, did not break the spell. She was still hanging around in unknown territory. Something in her was still frozen.

Suddenly she heard a voice saying, "I would suggest you move into that area within you that feels numb."

She looked up and shrank back. She had stared directly into the jackal face of Anubis. His brown eyes were calm and peaceful, but still, it was a shock to see his animal features in daylight, here, across the table in this noisy café. Then his face changed into its human form. She sighed and relaxed. He was wearing plain jeans and a white shirt.

I recognize those eyes so well, she thought. I have even begun to love this jackal face of his.

"Are you listening, Clara?" he asked, interrupting her flow of thoughts. His mouth had not moved, but his question still reached her.

"Close your eyes, Clara. I will take care of you. You are safe here in this place. "

She tumbled through space. Light flashed up irregularly, illuminating scenes oddly familiar to her. There was a village square where she was in the middle of a group of people who shouted at her and accused her of witchcraft. In the background, a huge bonfire crackled menacingly. She saw herself wrestling with brutal hands that reached out to her. She wanted to run away, but they held her tight. She was out of her mind with panic.

Then another scene invaded her mind. She laid at the bottom of a heavy wooden cross, an unutterable grief heavy within her as a man hung high above her, writhing in pain. "I am one with you," he screamed into the empty sky. Streams of tears coursed down her face. Again, she wanted to run away, but this time, an iron will of hers forced her to stay, to be witness, to bear the pain and not leave this man on the cross.

The scene changed again, and she saw herself in a train compartment that looked like a cattle wagon. Many people were crammed in, far too many for the small space. Babies wailed, and people panicked. Someone in a Nazi uniform slammed a heavy door shut, causing her body to jerk. Pain and anxiety filled her, and every cell in her body seemed to be bursting with anxiety. Claustrophobia and panic crawled up her spine and into her head. In a moment, she would explode into a thousand pieces, and madness would take over.

Her heart leapt when Anubis touched her hand and slowly stroked it with his fingers. He sat beside her, and she felt his nearness without opening her eyes. His warm breath caressed her face and his cheek lightly brushed her skin. She held her breath, wondering if she had imagined all those images. How real were they?

"Breathe through them, my love," he murmured into her ear. "Breathe through those images of horrors, and do not let yourself be carried away by them."

She squeezed his hand. "Oh Anubis," she whispered. "There is so much pain. How can I possibly endure so much pain?"

"Don´t go into the contraction," he said. "Imagine stretching your body into the space around it. Feel how you are stabilizing yourself in your own center. Stay the sacred witness. I am here to support you."

"It will break me. I know I will not survive this pain."

"It will only break the walls around your heart. It will set your heart free. You will feel so much more alive. You will never want to go back to that numbness again. Breathe, Clara, breathe!"

Slowly she sucked in a long, deep breath. Her lungs expanded, and her chest became larger. She felt as fragile as glass, and she was afraid that the expansion in her chest would shatter her body into a thousand glittering pieces. To her relief, her body did not burst. Her breathing soon returned to normal. When she visualized herself expanding into the space around her, she noticed with relief that the spell was losing its power.

She already wanted to open her eyes when another image turned up in her head.

With unrelenting sharpness, she saw guillotines in the midst of a crowd of villagers silhouetted against a tormented sky. Three men performed their jobs, again and again and again. The stream of people to be killed - young, old, even children - seemed endless. Clara watched as white shadows left their human bodies before the splitting blade hit their necks. The blade was ruthlessness, and pools of blood formed below the guillotines. The crowd shouted and cheered. A wave of energy rushed into her. She felt exhilarated. At the same time, Clara recognized a cold cruelty within her, a cruelty deprived of any compassion. She was determined to do her job, and she knew she did it well. The exhilarating power she experienced within her was tremendous. It was the power of experiencing herself as a towering person of power—someone who sends others into their own death.

With a tremoring jolt, Clara opened her eyes. She looked right into his attentive face. In his brown eyes, she did not see any emotion or judgement.

"Yes, Clara," he said after a moment. "You have been both. You were the victim, and you were the murderer. In many of your lifetimes, you played both roles. Never have you only been the victim."

She stared at him, horrified by the murderous frenzy that had just rushed through her body. Its power still vividly resonated in her veins.

"What a . . . monstrous power . . ." she said, barely hearing her own words. She hid her face behind her hands.

"This power is pure life force," he answered. "It is neither good nor bad. And it is always yours. You do not need to choose between the victim and the murderer. You can stand in your full power without playing any of those roles."

"How could I—do—do . . . this?" she asked.

"You see . . ." he paused for a moment, "when you suffered from the karmic consequences of being the murderer, you chose to never experience this power again. It is yours, though. You have been denying yourself the power of the shadow. It is time to acknowledge and release it now, Clara. Accepting those murderous emotions and taking full responsibility for the dark sides within you—*without playing them out*—that is which makes you whole. Do you understand, Clara?"

His voice was now quite pressing. "It is really important that you understand without judging yourself. You will not release much contracted energy if you begin to condemn yourself again. Instead, you will be creating new knots within yourself."

She nodded slowly. "I understand. I am so sorry. I am so incredibly sorry."

Anubis looked at her respectfully. "I know you are," he said. "Having compassion for everybody, including yourself, makes healing possible. Then you are truly transforming your demons into love."

I will never forget that I played both roles, Clara thought. They shall never again have a grip on me.

She also promised herself that she would never use that power against another human being again. She would never forget that strong, powerful current rushing through her body. She would always be able to tune into that power. She would, however, always approach it with the utmost respect and humbleness.

"It is yours," she heard Anubis's words echoing in her head. "In all its might, this power is yours."

* * *

She felt lonely. And cold. She had forgotten to switch on the heating in her apartment when she left for work that morning. Now it was late afternoon, and she sat in her armchair wrapped in a blanket. Soon, all daylight would be gone. A long and lonely evening threatened to spread out in front of her. At least that was how she felt. For today, Marco had given up his calls to convince her to meet again soon. She did not see any reason for it. Why should they? Nothing had really changed since they last met. Besides, she needed more time to figure out how to integrate her experiences with Anubis into her normal life.

I seem to be living in two universes simultaneously—in the ordinary world, and this other, non-physical, fantasy world, she thought.

"Why do I feel so isolated?" she asked herself, and her voice sounded desperate to her own ears. "Will I ever be able to feel whole?"

"What about further explorations with me?" she suddenly heard him asking. "You should know by now that I am always here waiting for you to call upon me."

"I know, and I don't know," Clara said meekly. Tears ran down her cheeks. With effort, she said, "I *am* grateful. I can feel you. But you are not here in physical form. You are just a—a ghost!"

"Oh, thank you," he said and chuckled. He materialized in front of her in blue jeans and a white T-shirt with a print of a golden serpent on its front. This time, his long black hair was bound together at his neck. Had he not the golden serpent on his shirt, one would mistake him for a middle-aged Indian tribesman.

He turned serious and moved to kneel in front of her. When he bent his head, he was so close that she could have put her hands on his head. He stayed like that, motionless. Was he waiting for her to make a move?

"Would you please allow me to touch you?" he offered quietly. "You might feel less lonely."

Clara backpedalled for a moment. Would she open herself to such an experiment?

"Please," he begged.

She only nodded and closed her eyes. Why had it suddenly become so quiet? Footsteps sounded, and she knew he had moved around her. In the all-encompassing silence, the ticking of her wall clock changed into a very distinct and sharp clangor. She tensed. Then she sensed Anubis raising his hands and moving them slowly towards her shoulders. When he touched her, their warmth immediately permeated the tissue of her T-shirt. She held her breath.

How tense I am, she thought. There is so much anxiety in me. What is there to fear? Did I not believe I would trust him?

"Relax," he whispered. "I will not move much."

He was so close that his breath tickled her ears.

"I am so much looking forward to fully surrendering to this feeling of touching you with my hands," she heard him murmuring.

The sensation of him standing behind her was extraordinary. His strong presence left no doubt that he was *there*, right behind her. Each of his fingers pressed through her T-shirt, as did the palms of his hands. When she imagined him exerting tiny pressing movements with his fingertips, she noticed with surprise that he started doing so the very moment the image had surfed up in her mind. She became totally absorbed by his miniature gestures. Her muscles willingly gave way to his hands and relaxed. They were like molten wax, allowing his fingertips to move deeper into her tissues. Gradually, she began to feel safe with him, began to trust the reality of this amazing touch.

After a long time, he slowly moved his hands to the sides of her neck. She shivered. His soft fingers touched her bare skin, went lightly over it, until they found a new place to stay. There they rested for what felt to her an eternity.

She noticed her head involuntarily move back, and when she followed this impulse, he murmured, "Rest your head against my legs, if this is more comfortable for you, Clara."

She arched her neck, and her head touched the soft cotton material of his skirt. It felt good to lean against him. She had begun to drift further into letting go. Unexplainably, tears filled her eyes. On a deeper level, she realized she was releasing tensions she had held for a long time. It felt so good to let go!

After a while, she raised her hands to search for his fingers. The touch of their fingertips caressing one another was exquisite, and slowly they began to explore each other's fingers, the sides and the hidden curves, their muscles, veins, and knuckles. Then they began to twist their fingers around each other. Clara felt them like branches of a tree enlacing each other. They held hands, as if those were the last hands they would ever hold.

I will never let go of his hands, she thought, feeling the liquid of her tears drying on her cheeks.

Then she gently pulled his fingers towards her upper chest. He was now half embracing her from behind, and the insides of his upper arms warmed her ears. She felt held and comforted like never before in her life. It was as if the two worlds she lived in were merging into each other, here and now, with his fingers entangled in hers and hers in his.

* * *

"You must have moved into your KA body," Erna said thoughtfully the next day, rubbing her nose. "You might have experienced him through your KA body, not your real body."

"But I did feel his fingers on my skin," Clara protested. "It was as real as this . . ." and she gave Erna a quick slap on her arm.

"Ouch!" Erna wailed and pretended to hit back. "Why can't you give me a massage like the one you had the pleasure to enjoy?"

"You are like a solid rock, my friend, and I am not quite there yet," Clara retorted.

"What do you mean, 'not quite there'?"

"I mean I am not even close to being called *enlightened*."

* * *

She awoke early in the morning. The room was still shadowy. She looked at the illuminated crystal stone which she had carefully placed onto a small, square, metal plate the night before. The sharp white LED light in the center of the plate pierced through the crystal, throwing tiny sparkles at the room's walls. There was hardly any noise, only some muffled and indistinguishable sounds from the city's nightlife.

Clara inhaled deeply. An unfathomable, mystical promise filled the darkness. The impression was so strong that it seemed tangible to her. She switched on the light and looked around. Everything was as she had seen it last night, and yet the stillness brimmed.

Clara took a sip of water and switched off the light again. She kept her eyes wide open, as if they could penetrate the darkness and reach the core of its deeply hidden truths.

Nothing happened.

She waited a while longer. Finally, she gave up.

No secrets to explore here, she thought. At least no secrets to which I am permitted access. She closed her eyes.

The image of two small flames leapt in front of her. She sensed that one flame represented her, and when she silently asked about the other flame, the word *Anubis* flashed in her head. The two yellowish flames flickered side by side in a rather stable and contained manner, without touching. Soul flames, she thought with rising awe. They might be our soul flames—or at least, sparks of them.

What would happen if I merge the two soul flames and make them one?

The thought excited and bewildered her at the same time. She held her breath. Would she dare to do this? Also, would she be allowed to do this at all?

She searched within herself and found no resistance. No warning voice held her back. At the same time, her heart contracted and her hands became hot. What would happen if her flame let his flame fully in? Would she open herself to forces and powers beyond her control? She might just vanish off the face of the earth!

"Anubis," she asked in a hushed voice. "Anubis, may I unify those two flames?"

Silence surrounded her. She blinked and closed her eyes again.

Without warning, the image of Anubis appeared. He stood in front of Clara. His hands were folded in front of him, as if forming a rung of a ladder. He nodded, indicating that he wanted Clara to leap onto his hands.

She thought, does he want me to step up? Her stomach tied into a knot.

Carefully, she put one foot on his hands, and with effort, she hoisted herself upward. The force of his hands lifted her, while paradoxically, the sensation of energy coming down entered her. It was as if two elevators moved within her—one going up, the other going down.

Then it dawned on her: there were no flames *outside her* to be merged. They were both inside. Anubis raising her up had somehow made her aware of his soul flame within her.

A warm sensation stirred deep in her womb. She could see the two flames dancing there, in her womb, below her navel. How amazing, she thought as she held her breath. Would she dare to continue? Still, she hesitated.

"Do not worry," she heard Anubis saying from afar. "I am with you. No harm will come to you. You need to voice your intent, though. It is not up to me to make this decision."

She knew what to ask. She silently called upon the two flames to merge. Then she saw them moving closer and closer, until their silhouettes touched. For a split second, they seemed to part, then they slowly moved into another.

Then they were one: one big and bright flame of glowing light, much stronger and much more powerful than the two singular ones.

Clara sighed. The warm sensation in her womb expanded at an amazing speed, and an immense wave of love rushed into her, inexplicably sweet and ravishing. White light exploded its brilliance in her third eye. Her awareness moved into her head. More explosions occurred, some tiny, some big. She became aware of a stream of energy connecting her womb with her third eye. A column of light shone in the central axis of her body. She straightened up and for a brief moment, clenched her fists. When she released them, she felt energy like a cool soft spring breeze running through her body. It calmed her down and she felt whole, whole within her body, and at the same time, in tune with everything outside. For seconds, she glimpsed ecstasy. She knew the union of the flames was complete.

"This is the Djed Pillar," she heard Anubis explaining. "It is the central channel of your spine. You are on the sacred path to transform your shadows, my love, and it is in the Djed, where your shadows are held in place. Soon, your spinal column will be a clear and open conduit between the heavens and the earth."

The white column of light remained stable for quite some time. After a while, the column became smaller, as if it had withdrawn into itself. She realized other thoughts had entered her mind, and although she had not wanted any distractions, her concentration faded. The sensations in her body ebbed away. The sounds of the city night crept into her ears again. Reality moved back into her life.

Clara opened her eyes, staring into the night. "Thank you," she whispered. "Thank you."

* * *

Later, she asked Anubis, "Why was I so hesitant to merge those two flames, Anubis? Could it be dangerous?"

"You have set up defenses to protect your heart. When you open up and allow the unknown in, you feel vulnerable. You intuitively know that you might be challenged by both your and the other being's shadows."

He reached out and brushed a strand of hair out of her face. "If it throws you out of center, you understand that there is still something to be mastered and transformed. It is normal that you hesitated. It takes so much courage to open up."

* * *

"Clara, were you not afraid of losing your individuality?" Erna's eyes were as round as two glistening dewdrops in the sun. "You might turn into one big, unidentifiable mass of . . . of . . . of whatever!" Red spots appeared on her skin, and she was obviously quite thrown off balance. "I would never have done this, Clara! Either you are very courageous, or you have lost your common sense."

Clara shook her head. "I had a commanding sense of myself as an individual being. The experience actually enhanced my sense of individuality, while at the same time I felt unified with Anubis. I felt more energetic. I understood, from Anubis, that it would be the same kind of energy that I had used before to protect myself." She took a sip of water. "The opening is scary. The union, however, was amazingly energizing. Anubis said that, when consciousness and love meet in a moment of openness and vulnerability, there is pure ecstasy. Apparently, it all happens within oneself, and it affects our outside as well. He also suggested that I explore it with Marco."

Clara started wrestling with her hands. "I am far from being ready for that! But I will at least open myself to the possibility."

A provocative glint flashed in Erna's eyes. "Would you like to practice with me?" she asked theatrically.

"No way!" Clara fended off her friend, grinning. "I would not be able to face all your shadows within me, Erna." She smiled. "You know I love you, my friend, but I am not on a mission to save you here."

She giggled at Erna's indignant expression. Then she sighed. "Those two worlds I live in . . . how am I ever going to bring them together?"

"Well, try it with the merging of the flames," Erna said dryly.

Clara looked at her, and they both started to laugh.

* * *

"You look sad, my beloved. What happened?" Anubis gently stroked Clara's head. Then he lifted her face and gazed straight into Clara's eyes.

His eyes are limitless, open gateways into a star-filled universe, Clara thought.

"Will you please tell me what is going on?" he asked softly. "There is much heaviness around you. So much heaviness. Let me know. Don't lose your awareness of how you are in this moment."

"I looked into Marco's eyes." Her voice broke, and she turned her face away from his.

"And?" he asked tenderly.

"There was nothing—nothing but bleakness," she said. "There was no real connection, neither to me, nor to anything else. It was as if his eyes were closed. It was as if an invisible wall stood between us, and I ran against it, crashing again and again. Even my body felt bruised."

"You have gone through the experience of being unmirrored," he said slowly.

"I know this feeling—I remember it from a long time ago," she said. "Where does it come from?"

He sighed. "Did you know that babies ultimately die when they are unmirrored? If you had absent parents, or depressed ones, if they did not pick you up again and again when you were crying, did not copy your facial expressions so that you understand that you are being noticed, you were missing a very important mirror in your life, Clara. It is an extremely fearful experience, because something in you does not feel seen and thus doubts your very existence. You are in fear of your own annihilation. Paradoxically, this experience is a portal back into the void from where you came."

He paused for a moment, then he asked, "You know the story they have been telling you about me, don't you?"

Clara rubbed her nose, then nodded. "You had been abandoned in the desert. Do you have any memories of this?"

"Memories float up in your consciousness when the right time has come to transform them," Anubis said. "I am well aware how it felt to be a baby looking up into the blue sky, and there was no one there for many many hours. There was no face to calm me, no one giggling with me, imitating my grimaces, nothing. I needed to go through the fear of annihilation myself. This is abandonment in its cruelest form—and most of the time, no one meant any harm. Many children in modern societies are unmirrored. It is a real tragedy. Children learn everything from ever-changing, vivid facial expressions. The television screen is by no means a mirror. Children need human faces as mirrors. You were triggered by Marco being absentminded. Then those memories surfed up."

"I understand," Clara said slowly. "And I do see, of course, how many times I absently thought about something else, how I myself was lost in my own stories when he expected me to listen. There is nobody to blame, really."

"No," Anubis said, shaking his head. "Never, actually. But it is good to see what is going on. Awareness without judgement always changes the energy of the situation. You will be able to find new pathways to deal with the situation."

Clara stared out of the window while tugging on a strand of her hair.

"Did Marco realize that something was going on?" Anubis asked.

"He appeared exhausted. The second before he acknowledged it, weariness came over me too, as if his exhaustion was a wild animal jumping at me. It was bewildering. Then I felt lonely. I remember I wondered where this sudden drop in energy came from."

"And then?"

"Then he decided to take a nap. Only after some minutes, though, he jumped up and became active again. Time to get up, go to work, make some calls, organize his day, he said. He avoided a straightforward look, but threw one of those questions across the room, such as, 'Are you okay?' He probably felt that there was something awkward in our relationship, but did not feel like inquiring any further. He was not waiting for my answer. He left the room, and I was on my own. His running away in that moment hurt me more than my feelings of separation and loneliness."

"Your awareness of this was a new experience for both of you," Anubis said. "A new angle that illuminated issues that have been pushed aside, uncomfortable feelings you both did not want to deal with. Those situations are always an opportunity to connect with something deeper in yourself. If you both are open and willing to experience and let through all your feelings, you would reach a new level of understanding of your relationship."

Clara nodded. "We were both evasive," she agreed.

She rubbed her eyes briskly. "Anubis, I do not know where to go with this man. My longing to be in a deeper relationship is so strong."

"Can you see the lessons for you in this?" Anubis asked cautiously. "It is an initiation into something much bigger than you are currently able to perceive."

Clara knit her brows, looked at him, then nodded. "I can see myself being called to be more present. I can see how important it is to go through my own fears and be compassionate. I do not want to be thrown off my center."

Anubis cocked his head. "You are practising the balancing of your own masculine and feminine power within you. You will become strong enough to hold both vibrations within yourself."

"In the meantime . . ." He smiled.

Clara looked up expectantly.

"In the meantime, he is being called to integrate the new information. He will, gradually. Sometimes it takes time for the physical to readjust to what there is already. Will you stay patient?"

She sighed. "What if he chooses otherwise?"

"If his resistance is too strong for him to overcome, he will leave." Anubis looked at her with gentleness in his eyes.

"There will be a period of grief, my love. There will be new space for new experiences. On a soul level, you will know that this is only positive. Your soul knows that you cannot be with a person who holds resistance against your longings to go deeper. Your pain of letting go of Marco will be as strong as your attachments to issues such as status or security. You might shed them more easily if you concentrate on what is calling your soul. This is how you step up to your own true power."

Anubis rubbed his hands. "Let us do an exercise," he suggested, and when she nodded, he said, "Look into my eyes. I will demonstrate to you some of the many different versions of how eyes can look."

When she did as he told her, she immediately pulled back. His eyes seemed impermeable. They were like a wall of concrete that bounced her back with violence she could almost feel physically in her body. It felt like a slap in the face—short and sharp and painful.

"This hurts," she exclaimed.

"My eyes are hostile," he said calmly. "I do not want you to see me truly, as I have something to hide, something so big that I cannot even look at it myself. It is just too big for me. It might be shame buried deep within me."

He paused, then went on. "My eyes warn you. Don't you dare come closer and mirror to me through your own eyes what must always remain my biggest secret. Don't you dare!"

Clara shuddered. "I know this," she then said slowly, "Often, those hostile eyes turn away because they do not want to keep the connection."

"Yes," Anubis said. "Now, let us try out those eyes."

When Clara looked into his eyes this time, she became insecure as to where to look and what to concentrate on.

"They are fleeting," she said, after a while. "It makes me feel desperately lonely to look into them. I have the strong impulse to look away, because there is nothing to hold onto. They seem to be there, and at the same time, they do not seem to be there." She shuddered. "Somewhat ghostly, those eyes."

Anubis nodded. "I am retreating. I have left my eyes open, but they are not focused. They seem to spill over to the edges and do not give you any orientation—just movements on the surface of water, no entrance to the depths beneath them. It is a similar veil as with the first expression, but less aggressive."

"Now," he smiled cheerfully, "let us turn to a nicer experiment."

When they looked into each other's eyes this time, Clara was drawn to move closer. She experienced his eyes as a gentle invitation to drop ever deeper into the connection and to open herself more and more to their meeting. There was a moment when Clara felt the movement of opening within her body. It was a sweet and ecstatic movement which first flickered over her skin, then drew her awareness to her second chakra, the womb inside her.

At that moment Anubis looked at her and grinned. "You see, my love, my open and receptive eyes create an immediate effect, causing you to open. Deep inside me, I tell you that I welcome you as my woman, and I want to experience you to the fullest possible extent. I let you enter my heart and feel you there and embrace you fully."

"With another person, I would immediately shy back, thinking that this is too close," Clara mumbled. "Those kinds of looks are far too intimate, I feel."

Anubis nodded. "With those eyes, all shame is invited to reveal itself for transformation. Shame is simply suppressed life energy circling within you. In truth, it is the energy of joy, of truly being connected with another person. You turn this energy into shame in no time. It falls down like a veil over your eyes. You turn your eyes away, because you do not want the other to reveal how much you are touched by this intimacy."

Anubis sighed. "The world is bereft of this intimacy, Clara. Many men and women move around rather ghostly, trying to be unnoticed, themselves not noticing others in their fields. It can be very lonely here on this planet, although it is a wonderful planet and provides everything you need to live a full and joyful life. You are slowly waking up. Eyes are reflecting this awakening; they become deeper and more meaningful and more connected with your own heart. It is like a muscle which has not been exercised for a long time. You must exercise it, and you will, because you will all be moving much closer together in the future. In fact . . ." Anubis laughed, "in fact, you will become aware that you are already one consciousness penetrating and influencing each other continuously on many different levels. It is great to experience this, my beloved. Once you get over your residues of shame, you will enjoy it. I promise!"

There is such longing and no, I will not allow it to be fully felt within me. Instead, I push it away.

I will not allow it to be here, to take its rightful place.

I know how it feels to be alive, and I know I am suppressing my life force.

I do not allow my longing to surf up.

I am afraid of being swept away.

In the night, when I am connected with those other realms of reality, I follow the call to ride the light waves of ecstasy. But right now, here, there is a clear no.

No, I will not permit my longing to devour me.

At the same time, I am asked . . . to pay respect.

To pay respect and acknowledge its presence.

There is a shift. Did I shift? Did the longing shift? Or possibly both?

It dawns on me there is nothing I can do to avoid the longing.

Something has shifted. Now I feel free. Acknowledging my

longing set me free.

My longing, the hissing, menacing snake, calmed down. She is now at peace.

Whenever I connect with what is, it can spiral itself into another place —a more spacious, more loving, and peaceful place.

All I did was acknowledge what is.

* * *

"Forget it," he said with a crystal-clear voice, and there was a sound as if he had shuffled his feet.

She looked up, startled. There he stood, a few meters away, in the center of a group of people who were discussing where to sit. The restaurant was packed, as usual at this time of day. He was not noticed by any of the guests, in spite of his stunning appearance. He wore a bright brown, long leather skirt with blue and golden hieroglyphs, a white T-shirt with a yellow sun painting on the chest, and leather sandals. His long, shiny black hair was held back tightly, which gave him an austere ambiance. He stood taller than most people around him, his head above most everyone else. He looked at her calmly. The noise in the restaurant was ear-splitting. Clara, however, had heard his words clearly.

"What are you doing here?" she said to him in her mind. She raised her hand and waved him to come nearer.

He shook his head almost imperceptibly. "Forget it," he said.

Her hands clenched. "What do you want me to forget?" she shot back in her thoughts.

"Forget about getting involved with another man. First, you must find out who you are and marry your masculine and feminine sides within you. This is your homework. Stay present, for Ma'at's sake, and don't get lost in the illusion of finding *it* out there."

She felt caught. How did he know that she had just been thinking of a man she had just met? More anger surged up within her.

"What do you have to do with this?" she asked in her thoughts. "Mind your own business, Anubis. I won't let you dictate to me what to do or dream. You are becoming quite a despot, my dear."

He started to move towards her, his eyes firmly fixed on hers. Then he began to laugh. "If looks could kill . . ." he said, visibly amused. "You can do whatever you want. I am just representing the masculine voice within you."

When she still scowled at him, he said in a conciliatory voice, "I am your inner truth, Clara. Do not project anything else onto me. It is your inner truth which was spoken so clearly. It is your own power which I mirror to you. I only mirror what is inside you. So release your reproaches, my love, and be proud of yourself." He sat down and reached out his hand to touch her.

She hesitantly put her hand in his. "But why is there such longing?" she said with a strenuous voice.

"It is your soul longing to realize what you are already in the deep. The longing is a calling home to your real state of being, where there is no lack. It says, you already *are* what you long for."

Clara blinked. *Does he expect me to understand this?*

"You can project all your longings onto the other," Anubis explained. "You will only create attachments on all levels. You immediately move out of your own circle of power. You know that."

"Yes." She nodded reluctantly. She had gone through all this.

"So stop it," Anubis said emphatically. "Stop it, right now. Move into the holographic reality of already being one with 'the beloved.' You will immediately notice the shift. Immediately. When you feel as one, you are one; you are radiating out that you are one, and everything out there will adjust to this new reality. There will be no scarcity, if you live in fullness. Trust me, Clara." He was watching her closely.

"I, as the masculine within you, am holding you tight with my eyes. Surrender to the divine love within me and release your longing into the holographic reality of this life here on Earth."

He knelt in front of her and looked up. "Do not shove your circle of power underneath another being's circle by making yourself dependent on him or the situation to fulfill your longings, Clara. Please stay clear. You don't want to go all the way around another loop of illusion."

Clara looked into his piercing, intense eyes, which were also loving, as always, and deeply caring.

She closed her eyes briefly. Then she said, with exhaustion in her voice, "I know exactly what you mean, Anubis. I know exactly. But it is such a strong pull."

Clara took a deep breath. "The woman in me longs to surrender, to be washed away," she said with a low voice.

She began moaning. Her moaning became more forceful. It filled her body, it took over, and she bent at the waist. An image in her head surfed up, the image of all forms around her shaking and tumbling and finally coming down in a gigantic earthquake. Everything around her lost its solidity, all objects in the restaurant; tables, chairs, food, and even the people seemed to be jolted from a relentless and invisible power within her. At the same time, her body trembled vigorously. The whole world seemed to come down around her in a towering shake.

The image faded and also her moaning subsided. A strong feeling of immense freedom rushed into her. She gasped.

He looked at her attentively. Then he smiled. "Everything okay?"

She only nodded. Everything had moved back to its place. Her body, though, still shook from the force. She was acutely aware of her bones vibrating quietly.

She lowered her head. "What was that?" she asked.

"You must have called for Wadjet, the great cobra goddess of Egypt."

"Wadjet?" Clara asked, puzzled.

"Wadjet purifies your motives. She shakes your ego structure so that nothing is in the way and the energy can rise. She will infuse you with her life force when she deems you worthy. You must have called her with your exploration regarding your longing, and she responded."

He looked at her questionly. "I know you understood," he then said in a pleading voice. "Please, Clara."

She stared at him. Then she slowly nodded. She knew he was right. Living a life full of purpose was not a matter of fantasizing about any other man. It was about finally knowing her own true self and becoming whole within herself.

* * *

I am lying on the bare stones. My long hair is loose and tangled, my white cotton dress wet with tears. I am lying here while I experience the complete and utter drowning of myself in despair—a despair like a river of rushing water, relentlessly invading each cell of my body.

How often had I gone up those stairs, passed those mighty yellow sandstone columns, and entered the most inner of the Anubeion—the temple for the worshipping of the Weigher of the Hearts, the God of Embalmment? How often had I held the energy of the four divine Neters—Anubis, Thoth, Ma'at, and Osiris—together with two of my brothers and a sister to deliver the timeless wisdom to the assembled initiates? How often had I conducted rituals to worship Anubis, rituals which had been taught to me by the wise and knowledgeable ones, those priests and priestesses of the Anubeion who were there before me? They had taught me wisdom which had been passed on to them and their alikes for hundreds and hundreds of years in order for me to carry on their wisdom, to become a High Priestess myself.

Innumerable times I sat here in silence, in the complete and ecstatic merging with the divine. In the evenings, I often stayed longer than my brothers and sisters, in the presence of the dancing torches in the fainting light. Alone, I had connected with Anubis and practiced the sacred tantric rituals—ancient practices for the strengthening of my lightbody—for the physical manifestation of the divine within me.

Now I am lying here, devastated, and with a broken heart. The Egyptian era of thousands of years has come to an end. The reign has brutally been taken over by barbarians who have no intention to follow our sacred rules and defend our highest values. The decline of this culture is irreversible. This was the message I had just received in my meditation, clearly and with an anxious heart—a message I had long carried within me, a message I did not want to listen to. It had surged up in such clarity that there was no way for me to ignore it anymore. I knew we would need to leave this holy place, would go far away to another country, the name of which had not yet entered my ears due to precautions of the elders. There was fear of betrayal, betrayal from our own people.

You will be with me, I heard him saying. We are one.

I knew he was trying to soothe me.

It did not console me.

I had not forgotten how he once told me that there will be times when I would not even whisper his name once—times in which all sacred rituals were buried deeply in my own subconsciousness and mere survival would be my only priority. This would be in many of my future lifetimes, for many centuries. Only when the end of a world cycle was nearing would I be able to connect with him again. Only then would the vibrations of my energy field be high enough to be with him again. Thousands of years will have passed by. When those new times are dawning, the holographic reality of this universe and countless others will be revealed to me.

My heart was in immeasurable pain, and I had the feeling of falling into endless darkness. From afar, a sudden wind arose, bringing along with it a long breath carrying strange sounds. Murannah . . .Murannah . . . A vision of a head carved in dark stone pierced on a metal rod flashed up in my head and disappeared. I tried to remember, but there was no way I could. I sobbed wretchedly. There was nothing I could do. I was only allowed to surrender.

* * *

"He might be Anubis, too," Anubis said.

"What do you mean?" She turned around and glared at him. "There is only one Anubis!"

"Are you sure?" He let out high-pitched laughter.

She frowned, then turned back and looked across the blue lake. A splash broke the surface of the water a few meters away from her. She squinted. Nothing. The surface of the lake was an even, bleak mirror.

"It is a frequency," he said.

"What do you mean by *frequency*?" she snapped. She did not like the idea that there might be more than one Anubis out there.

"Well, frequency . . . what do you think it might stand for?"

She looked up, still feeling stubborn. "That is difficult to say," she then said, rubbing her nose.

"How do you perceive me when you see images of me on those Egyptian tombs?" he asked.

"It is serious work," she answered slowly.

"You are doing serious work. You are there when people die. You are weighing their hearts. You are a witness when their lives flash before their eyes. You see their paths, their decisions, their truths, and their lies. I guess you also sense their emotions when they go back through their lives in their minds. You are probably some sort of a super-empath."

She laughed.

He nodded. "Yes, I sense it all. However, I do not judge. I do not blame. I am the one holding the space for the sacred witness within those who just passed through the door to another realm—for them to be able to see and understand."

"Then . . ." Clara added reflectively, after a while, "you are also quite humble."

"I am her servant," he responded reverently. "I am serving Ma'at, the great goddess of justice and love. The masculine is to worship the feminine. The feminine is to surrender to the masculine. This is one of the secrets to the true balancing of the two polarities. As within so without. If a man does not worship the feminine within, how can he worship her outside?"

She cocked her head. "I feel your adoration for her. It is a wonderful feeling and so very unknown to me. A man worshipping a high female being. So much humbleness and love and respect. No begging or whining. Just worship."

She closed her eyes. "I see rituals. I see rituals, but there is not much noise. Everything is so peaceful. Everything is in the right order. You play your role with utmost serenity and seriousness. You know your place. It is as if you and the role you play are one—a perfect synchronicity."

She sighed. "I wish I knew my place, too."

"You are on your path to finding your place," Anubis reminded her.

"There is peace, because the rules are clear," Clara added, still reflecting on her vision.

"Yes," he confirmed. "Thousands of years of peace, because the rules were clear, and everybody knew them. There were forty-two rules to obey and forty-two high beings present at the day of death.

You would call them *judges* nowadays. They are manifestations of utmost integrity. They are of the light."

"How did it change?" Clara asked cautiously.

"Greediness and the strife for power, worldly power, took over. Before, everything had been spiritual, and there was no separation between the spiritual and the mundane. The spiritual penetrated everything in daily life. But then, the knowledge of how to use those spiritual powers for your own ego fell into the wrong hands." His face was twisted with pain for a moment.

"Gradually, the balance got lost. The priests and priestesses felt it first. Most of them tried to restore the balance, but some changed sides. They wanted power for themselves. They became interested in manipulating people by feeding their fears. It is a vicious circle. Those who became fearful felt it legitimate to use those powers to defend themselves. The split became deeper. It was as if heaven and earth had separated. Not much difference in your world today, if you ask me."

He paused pensively. "When the scale of Ma'at broke, many priests and priestesses had to take flight. They left their beloved temples and shrines. This was the end of a culture which had existed peacefully for many thousand years." He exhaled.

"There were many priests and priestesses worshipping me, the god Anubis. You were one of them, my beloved. Worshipping me means 'becoming me'—wearing my mask, slipping into my role, my features, my vibration, performing my tasks. There were many worshipping the principles I represent. Your man might want to express those in his films. That is what I mean when I say he might be Anubis, too.

"And then, just to add another dimension to this picture," Anubis paused and grinned mischievously, "do you know the Sphinx, Clara?"

"Of course I do."

"You read that her head is that of a lion. Have a close look at her body! It is actually long and slender. If you look more closely, you will see that her body does not really conform to a lion's head."

"It doesn't?" Clara raised an eyebrow.

"No," Anubis said.

Then it dawned on Clara. "Is it a jackal's body?" she asked breathlessly.

Anubis only nodded. He locked his eyes into hers. There was a moment of utter stillness.

Suddenly the air began to whirl as if creating a vortex. A tornado formed itself in front of Clara's eyes. It quickly filled with hot and wild sand being shoved out of the empty space in front of her.

Clara trembled. She felt dizzy. The sand filled the air around her, and she did not know how to breathe. There was a sharp cracking sound. Clara fell on her knees and covered her head to avoid breathing in the sand. The noise of the tornado deafened her, and she covered her ears. Just when she thought she could not stand it a moment longer, the noise slowly ebbed.

When she gained her equilibrium, she was at a completely different place. Darkness surrounded her, as did the scent of old stones, warm desert air, and, faintly, the fragrance of frankincense. Her hands and feet and part of her body rested heavily on the hard ground. She knew with impeccable precision that she had moved into the body of the Sphinx. She was not only *in it*, but she *was it*. She also instantly knew that, although she was made of stones, she was hollow inside, and that it was the vibration of Anubis who filled up every tiny space within and around her.

8

SURRENDER

In her dream, Anubis stood next to another being. The white light of myriad of stars sparkled in the firmament against the dark night sky.

"This is Serapis Bey," Anubis said. "He is the ascended master who lends his fingers and hands to all human beings reaching out in deepest despair for hope, for a signal, a sound, or a smell, confirming that nobody here on this planet is alone and that separation is an illusion."

Clara bowed down to this being whose name sounded only reasonably familiar to her, then her face lit up when she turned towards Anubis. How grateful she was that he had become part of her world! How much she enjoyed his serene presence, his quiet and reassuring love towards her!

She went up to him and, impulsively, she fell to her knees before him. He was her master: she had chosen him, as he had chosen her. She closed her eyes, and waves of relief and gratitude welled up in her body. She heard him moving to the ground as well. When he kneeled opposite her, she looked up at him. She felt her heart opening and took him in fully, acknowledging with the totality of her being his importance in her life. Heat burned within her chest, and an image of orange and yellow flames licking out of her heart, growing stronger and stronger, flared in her mind. The flames ravished her and bent her backwards. It was as if her head was gently being pulled from behind so that her throat arched wide. A rush of energy floated up and down her throat, offering an exquisite sense of spaciousness. She felt a soft stirring within her womb. A stream of sweet and loving energy flowed all the way up from her womb, through her heart, into her throat and beyond. It felt pleasant and sweet. She fully surrendered to this stream of energy. Deep in her heart, she knew that this devotion of hers made her feel those sensations. She would be giving herself to him, always. She trusted him from the depth of her heart. She had indeed found the master within.

Then he touched her head.

"Stand up, my love," he said as love and compassion shined in his eyes. "Stand up." His eyes glowed with his admiration for her, his devotion, his encompassing, unconditional love for her. Tiny muscles moved in his face, their flickering indicating how much he was touched by her surrender to him. With a soft grip he drew her towards him and embraced her.

He murmured in her ear, "I will always be at your service, Clara. I will always worship you as my woman, as I have done for many centuries. I will take care of you, and I will never let you go."

With those words, he drew her even closer. Their bodies melted into one another. No boundaries existed. They dissolved into a space beyond, a space which held both passion and stillness together at the same time. What remained was an ever-growing feeling of oneness, love, and presence.

When Clara woke up, she knew that they had stood like this for a long time. It was as if they had been in a holographic capsule beyond time and space, as if the sensation of oneness had rippled out into eternity and flowed back to those two bodies, then out again, in an eternal cycle of expansion and contraction.

* * *

"How could I learn devotion, Clara?" Erna asked breathlessly after Clara had described her dream in arid words.

They sat on spinning bicycles at their local gym, where they had agreed to meet. They were nearly through their workout time and already in their cooling-off phase, having ridden the bicycles like people running for their lives.

Clara shook her head fervently. "I have no idea," she said, wiping the sweat off her forehead with her arm. "I do not find it easy to move into that vibration either, except in my dreamtime. When I asked Anubis about it, he said you open a space for it, and you must be devoted to devotion. Isn't that a great explanation? What does this mean, devoted to devotion? It is so typical for him, to elucidate it like this."

Erna looked at her with a stern impression on her face.

"It makes a lot of sense to me," she said, panting. "There is not much devotion in modern-day life. It is not really a treasured value these days. We are all dashing around in a frenzy. Even the so-called spiritual people are hurrying to becoming whatever they wish to become: enlightened, whole, masters of light. It is all about one's self, one's own progress and path, or purpose, however you want to call it." Absentmindedly, she followed one of the gym teachers with her eyes.

"Devotion seems to be a portal into a different realm of beingness," Erna then said reflectively. "It might actually not be as boring as I always thought."

She laughed out loud. "It might even be pretty ferocious! In its fierce calling to surrender and let go, it calls for a perfect balancing of our yin and yang energies."

She turned around to Clara, beaming with joy. "I believe I just understood something here, Clara! This is fascinating. I will definitely explore it. I mean, I will set my intent to be in a devotional state more often."

With those words, Erna swung her legs over the bike and hopped off.

* * *

"Time for a couple of love lessons. Would you like to join me, Clara?" He pointed to her bed.

"What do you mean?" Clara asked, alarmed. "Usually you just disappear into the air. What do you mean with love lessons?"

"Don't you want to invite me into your bed?" Anubis's eyes sparkled with an impish twinkle.

"Well . . . yes!" Clara exclaimed. All of a sudden, she felt shy.

"Let us go then," Anubis said. He grabbed the bottle of red wine and one glass and motioned her to take her glass, too. "Who knows how long this night will be."

Clara was speechless.

He put one arm around her and moved her gently towards the king-sized bed.

"And what now?" Clara was able to ask in a matter-of-fact voice. She was trying to come to grips with this new turn of events.

He did not respond. Instead, he put the bottle of wine and the glass onto the sideboard. She watched him take off his T-shirt. His slender brown body shimmered in the dim lights of the room. Outside, the night had come down, and a soft breeze blew through the open terrasse door.

Clara laid on the bed, watching him. Uneasily, she moved her body until she found a comfortable position. Then she sighed.

With a start, Anubis closed the shutters. Only a small gap remained, and through this gap the silvery moonlight fell into the room and shined across the wooden floor and onto the bed. Anubis turned around and came up to Clara. He took her face into his hands and looked into her eyes.

"You do not feel very safe, my love," he said softly. "What can I do to calm you down? Would you allow me to give you a hug?"

Clara nodded. Then she wrapped her arms around his body. His faint scent teased her nose, a fragrance with which she was so familiar by now. It reminded her of Lapacho tea—sweet and light with a trace of wood in it.

Her body relaxed in his warm embrace. Her shoulders dropped, and a flowing movement eased from the back of her head down into her spine.

He drew her closer to him. "Please concentrate on your root chakra," he murmured into her ear. "Imagine its vibration becoming a coherent vibration with mine."

Clara closed her eyes. Silence filled the room, a kind of silence filled with incomprehensible secrets and promises. A warm wave of energy made itself known in her womb. It was nearly unnoticeable, but the warmth spread down her legs and up into her chest.

Anubis switched off the lights, and darkness rushed in. Slowly, he began to undress her. She remained motionless and did not dare to breathe. This was all very new to her. She heard him taking the almond oil from the table beside her bed. She stretched out naked, and he began caressing her body with his hands, first around her navel, in very slow and circular movements, massaging the oil into her skin. Her body slowly started to surrender to his hands.

"Enjoy my hands, my beloved," he murmured. "Feel how I am moving my consciousness into my fingers and fingertips. We have an eternity to worship those sacred bodies of the earth. Let us celebrate her."

***

Anubis did not move. He did not move at all within her. Even his head did not waver. His face hovered above her, watching her with tender and attentive eyes, holding her with his gaze. From afar, the sounds of the church bell rang midnight. Then stillness settled in again. She had the impression of space expanding within her, endlessly and inexorably. At the same time, she perceived herself as floating in space, floating in a black sky filled with innumerable stars. In spite of this impression of expansion, time seemed to stand still.

Her vagina was warm and moist. His penis was completely enclosed by her. He was deep inside her, resting there in an utmost state of awareness, a state of immense intensity, devoid of any movements.

A wave of warmth flooded up towards her heart and filled her with peace. How much she enjoyed his presence in her! How much she enjoyed the motionless state of his being within her! She relaxed more into his undeviating presence. Instantly, she felt his response within her. The movement was immeasurably small. Maybe it was not even a movement; maybe it was a sparkle of a tiny flicker of electricity, some electrons changing locations, maybe even switching bodies. Another wave of warmth surged up within her, slowly crescendoing to a euphoric feeling of lightness and love.

He moaned. Then he bent his head towards her and whispered, "This is endless, Clara. The opening and the expansion is endless, can you feel it? Can you feel how there is only vastness, expansion, and love?"

She nodded, her eyes still transfixed by his gaze. His eyes were her anchor. It was everything she had ever wanted. Gratefulness swelled inside her, creating movement around her heart. Something opened, a tiny opening, nearly unnoticeable, but at the same time so intense. She started to feel shaky. Only his tender eyes made her stay with the sensations and not lose attention. She perceived invisible layers of protection circling like rings of metal around her heart. One by one, they slowly dissolved into the nothingness the space provided until an image of a heart came up in front of her eyes, a heart throbbing softly and evenly.

"I am here," she murmured. "This is me, surrendering to this opening in the trance of those beloved eyes. This is me, in the process of shedding my protection, of becoming lighter and lighter. The more I open to this pure space, the more intimacy I experience." She surrendered even deeper to him.

"This is true communion on every level," he whispered. "I so much enjoy this with you. Your surrender emits waves of energy into my penis, my love. I am pulsating within you, thus penetrating you to the core. Can you feel it?"

She nodded. It is much more than surrendering to him, she thought. It is as if I am surrendering to the universe itself. As soon as the image of the universe appeared in her mind, a further opening within her occurred, along with an even stronger energy wave that moved through her. They both moaned at the same time.

Then she felt a soft pulling, as if a hand had stroked gently the strings of a violin. Once. Only once. A faint sound vibrated through her body, letting her drop deeper into the moment of now. There! There was the pulling again. It spinned in her womb like a miniature golden sun, then it moved outwards in ever widening spirals of gold. It created a sweet sensation in her womb. Her head bent back so that her throat arched upwards towards his head.

Anubis softly began kissing her throat. She surrendered every part of her body to him, to this feeling of vastness, this expanded feeling of being. He was right: the opening and the deepening were endless. When he softly caressed her lips with his mouth, ecstasy moved from her womb all the way up into her head. Suddenly, light flooded her head, an explosion of white-golden light. She opened her eyes only to drown in his, which were streaming love and appreciation for the intense oneness of the moment. This was the most intimate, and at the same time, the most impersonal love Clara had ever experienced in her life.

Then he smiled.

"You are sucking on me, my beloved. Do you notice it? Your vagina is sucking on me. It feels like a thousand tiny butterfly kisses, so wonderful, so delicate."

She smiled too. "For me, it is more a pulling," she said with a hushed voice. "A very soft pulling." She closed her eyes for a moment, then opened them again. "This is the sweetest feeling I have ever experienced," she murmured. "There is a pulling from my vagina into my womb. My womb feels like a cave, a cave expanding into space."

She shivered and calmed down again. Then her body jolted in a sudden movement. It brought her back into the moment.

"What was that?" she asked quietly.

"An energy knot," Anubis answered in a low voice. "We are circulating a lot of energy within our bodies, Clara. New pathways are being created."

He smiled lightly. "Sometimes, old pathways are blocked by energy knots. They can dissolve themselves within a millisecond. When their energy is being released, you experience those sudden twitches."

Then he began to slowly pull out of Clara.

"Let us get some sleep," he murmured. He kissed her softly on her neck and laid down besides her.

* * *

"So, was it real or not?" Clara asked impetuously.

An unfamiliar sound filled the air, like water rushing by at considerable speed. It sounded like a distant waterfall. A waterfall? she thought anxiously, moving her body.

With increased trepidation, she realised that the water around the boat had changed its appearance. A strong drift pushed and gurgled along the sides of the boat. Never had she experienced something like that before on this lake. When she arrived earlier at the cave, the lake's surface had maintained its usual tranquility. Now the water was obviously heading towards an invisible goal.

"Everything is real, and nothing is real," he answered. "Did your body not respond to the tantric practices I advised you to do? What happened when you imagined a wave of sea water gently flowing into your womb?"

Clara blushed. She did not say anything, but frowned and looked at the water as she tried to figure out how to explain the extraordinary sensation in ordinary words.

Anubis watched her, amused. "Your muscles in your vagina responded to this image, right?" he said lightly. "They gradually relaxed into this sensation, correct?"

She nodded. She remembered that extraordinary feeling very well. The more she had relaxed, the stronger was the sensation in her womb.

"And then there was moisture, and it was real, too, wasn't it?" Anubis grinned. "So, now you wonder, did the water make love with you? Is this all a product of your imagination? When we make love, is this also only your imagination? Are you making love with a ghost?" His grin grew broader.

"So, *is* this all in my imagination?" she asked, impulsively lifting her gaze from the water.

She thought randomly, what the heck about the water? This topic is far too interesting.

"Well, you tell me," he answered.

She sighed. "I guess it was the energy," she said slowly. "It was the energy of the water merging with my energy in a place other than the physical realm. Strangely enough, my physical body also responded." She bit her lips.

"Strangely enough?" he asked teasingly. "Is this all you want to tell me? Wasn't it pleasant also?"

"Of course it was," she answered, slightly annoyed. "You know this, Anubis. I want to know—why is that so?"

He looked at her solemnly. "You are quite harsh with me now," he said, visibly amused. "I appreciate you wanting to know the truth, though. How can I explain?"

"Are we all one, or not?" Clara grew impatient. She nervously stared at the water again.

"We are all one within the universal soul. However, we are also an individualized soul fragment—that which had formed your body. If you merge with someone on the soul level, the shape of the bodily forms do not matter. It is a matter of imagination."

"But if I imagine water flowing into my belly, or you being inside me, where is the difference in using pornographic images for my own sexual arousal?" she asked as her eyes anxiously cruised the water.

"Not much difference on the physical level, if looked at superficially," he answered calmly.

"Pardon me?" Clara said, bewildered. She looked up.

"It is the same tool with seemingly the same effects. You use your imagination to stir up the energy. However, the emotional information transported in what you call pornographic images is vastly different from the information of a sea wave. Apart from the pleasure, you probably felt yourself expanding, and you were possibly a bit grateful, also." Anubis smiled.

"Very much so," Clara answered fervently, staring at the water again. Small waves danced on the surface, splashing white foam in all directions. It would have looked jolly if the water itself had not changed its color. It was now muddy gray, with streaks of dark blue.

"Feeling grateful is pure nourishment for your heart, my love. Your heart knows how to amplify the energy and let it flow back into your spiritual body. You are becoming aware of ever-more-subtle and deeper sensations within your body. Your joy deepens. You have created a most joyful cycle of energy, which actually strengthens all your lightbodies."

He paused for a moment. "With pornographic images, you are being carried away into no-man's or no-woman's land. As you are losing the sense of yourself, you are separating yourself more and more from what you truly are. During sex, you are also separating yourself from the other person. It might be called hot sex, but all that movement is merely an overstimulation of your system, which shut down long ago and which actually needs such strong stimulation in order to experience itself as being alive. The release comes at the point of the highest contraction. The energy is being thrust out and lost. Afterwards, often, you feel exhausted and disconnected." He bowed his head and gazed into the water.

"If you follow the other path, the path of the heart, you might get aroused by the softest breeze—or maybe not even a breeze at all, just a movement in consciousness. You will feel one with everything, and at the same time, you will perceive yourself as an individualized soul."

Anubis fell quiet before speaking again. "There is a thin but very distinct line in allowing the energy to be and staying with it in full awareness, or losing yourself in thoughts and images."

"I can see that," she said.

"It is a choice," he said lightheartedly. "You have chosen already. So what about the next exercise?"

She gave him a curious look. Then she noticed a sudden twist of the boat. "Anubis," she shouted with terror in her voice as she pointed to the front. A short distance away, a razor-sharp edge appeared. The ridge of the water stretched out horizontally like an unwavering line against a blackening horizon.

"Look!" she yelled. "The water is falling down! There is a waterfall! Can you stop the boat? Please, we need to turn, we need to head towards the coast! Quick, let us be quick!"

The noise of the nearing waterfall tormented her. Anubis, however, did not seem to be concerned. His face was like a stone.

"Loooooooook!"

Her cry fell useless against the noise of the rushing water. She stretched out her hand to grab his stick. She tried to grasp it, but he firmly gripped her hand. He looked at her intently. Words filled her head: *This is all about trust. Trust that you will be able to fly!*

She heard herself screaming in terror while he shouted, *"Now!"*

The boat tipped over the ridge. Its front hung helpless in the air before it began to drop down, shifting from the horizontal into the vertical, into the unknown, the abyss.

Clara saw every tiny movement in slow motion.

Somehow, she perceived herself both sitting on the wooden seat *and* hovering about six feet above the scene. She yelled again, and then she felt herself being lifted from the seat and catapulted into the air. Her vision blurred, and the only thing she was aware of was his hand holding her wrist. Then everything turned dark.

* * *

"So, did you actually fly?" Erna asked incredulously, after Clara told her of her experience. "I mean, did you actually see yourself flying in the air?"

"No," Clara said dryly. "I woke up with an aching wrist. It was all bruised, too. So I guess at least I did not crash and drown. Something held me there."

"It was Anubis holding you, Clara. Of course," Erna said, all excited. "This is phenomenal! He is such a good teacher!"

"Well, I think I pretty much screwed it up here." Clara rubbed her wrist. "And guess what? Whenever you screw up, you need to—"

"Do it again!" Erna said, exhilarated. "I know *that* rule!"

She gave Clara a pat on her back. "You will not lose consciousness next time, Clara. You will be able to fly! I will be so delighted to know that you have gone through *that* hole of the needle."

Clara only looked at her. "I see that you are ready for some of those lessons too," she then said mischievously. "I will introduce you to him, and then you just wait and see what kind of initiations he might give you. Get yourself ready, my beloved friend. Nobody will be able to escape. Do you hear me, Erna? In nowadays world, we are all being tested!"

With those words she turned around and left Erna behind, gasping.

* * *

"I can't believe you are in me!"

"Where else should I be?" he said with cheerful astonishment in his voice.

"I was looking outside all day long," she complained. "I was restlessly running around in the house, keeping myself busy with a thousand different things, first wondering, then increasingly desperately asking myself what is this all about? What the hell am I supposed to do now?"

"And then?" he asked.

"I forced myself to go outside and sit under a birch tree in the *Englischer Garten*," she answered. "I started drumming. My drum sounded flabby—the rawhide suffered from the humidity in the air. I started drumming, but it did not feel right. Then I imagined you in front of me, which did not feel right, either. Only when I realized you are within me, filling up my whole body, then . . ."

"What then?" he asked.

"It was magical," she responded, after a while.

When he scrutinized her, she turned away and gazed towards the distance. "There was a lot more movement within me. I felt you filling me up completely. It was as if you were caressing my body from the inside. It was the most tender feeling. It was like coming home inside me."

"You experienced presence itself, my beloved," he answered. "When you connect with me and with your body at the same time, your love fills up your energy body and spills over to your physical body. It moves as presence in your body. It can be quite delicious," he added mischievously.

"There was an instant reaction in my physical body," she admitted. "Sweet and ecstatic. Whenever I remind myself of you being a part of me, the energy is there—or maybe I just become conscious of the energy constantly pervading me. I feel whole. I do not miss anything in this state. All my wishes and longings come to rest within me."

"It is the light of love pervading you all the time," he explained. "Whenever you become conscious of it, you will experience the sweetness of it. I am just an image for you to surrender to this love and this light. Pure energy is moving through you."

"I feel insecure," she mumbled. "Am I crazy?"

"No. Think of the mystics of this world. Drinking the divine has enraptured them. Think of your Christian saints. They all experienced the ecstasy of being filled with God. It is the same experience. It is a vibration much needed on this planet. Also, it nourishes Mother Earth. More people than you might imagine are currently experiencing those phenomena. You are all strengthening the web that mystics have been weaving throughout time to facilitate the ascension of everybody. You are now part of the weaving, Clara. At the same time, you are the woven one. Just know that you are taking part in the mystical process of becoming whole."

* * *

They had taken off their clothes, slowly and without words, as if they were following a silent call. When she stretched out naked on the white sheets, she sighed. Then she reached out her arms and pulled him close to her. They curled up in each other's embrace, skin caressing skin wherever there was contact, their warm touch bearing recognition, remembrance, and validation.

When she withdrew from him for a moment, her gaze fell on his penis. She smiled. His penis laid on his thigh softly, like a snake resting. Her lower belly relaxed, and she gently drew him closer to her again.

Clara became aware of a serene stillness building itself up and wrapping around her like a warm cloth. Their breath became deeper and more regular, then there was the moment when she felt that they became one breath, filling the room. They were one with the serenity of the stillness.

Clara sensed a new movement, an invisible but clearly recognizable shift in the energy. She knew intuitively that he was now ready to enter her. She remembered him saying, "It is the field information which you are gradually able to begin to read." Now she understood what he meant. His penis was still soft, but there was new alertness in the air which held tremendous power. The energy had built up. It was powerful enough for him to slip into her, with his penis like a seal in a wave of water—gently, soft, but ready.

He grew inside of her. It was a slow growing, slow and very subtle. She knew she did not need to do anything. She had all the time in the world. His eyes remained perfectly calm. His face was relaxed and peaceful, and his brown skin shimmered with an unearthly glow. It was as if he were looking within, immersed in his body, but at the same time holding her with his tender gaze.

She felt seen.

There was a message in his eyes, in the way he looked both through and beyond her. She shivered. I have seen the past, she suddenly thought. I am the present. I know the future. The future – it is a place in the heart.

She understood. Each moment was vibrant with eternity.

Suddenly she perceived him as a steady column of light. He seemed to no longer have a will of his own. He had entirely given over the reigns to his penis, which was like an antenna, trusting that his penis would commune with her warm body and respond to her stirrings. She knew she had to let go of all the concepts and all the questions, let go of what should happen to her, to him, how she should move, how he would perceive her. She let them slip away like layers of skin, shedding herself of all of those false identities, like a snake. The only thing that mattered to her was his resting inside her and those subtle impulses she received from him, deep inside her womb. She responded in unnoticeable movements only his penis could perceive, before those sensations circulated within him and back to her. It was a circular electric current. Each tiny little growing of his penis was a tender movement towards more wholeness, more presence. There were long stretches of time where there seemed to be no movements at all. Not even movements of consciousness, she thought, amused. She continuously dropped deeper into their unified state of being. There was no end to it.

"Are you not afraid of losing your erection?" she asked him later.

"There is no fear within me," he said, shaking his head. "The energy ebbs and flows. It is like a wave. I focus on the joy from the presence of being within you and of my skin touching yours on the inside. I am not afraid. I have gone through that portal of death. My erection will come and go. I hold it up in my consciousness. On an energetic level, it cannot go away. As within, so without."

The cool white sheets brushed her skin. Once in awhile, the

candles flickered, responding to an invisible draft of air. They had all the time in the world. They barely moved. The space, however, was filled with unspoken meanings.

This is me belonging to the unknown, she randomly thought at one point. This is the most peaceful feeling I know, the feeling of belonging.

She knew she would never forget this state, this state where she felt complete and whole. She needed nothing. With this energy of love and presence circulating simultaneously in both their bodies, their boundaries ultimately dissolved. What remained was bliss beyond words.

* * *

Later, he said, "It is the intent. Men often lack the intent to enter the mysterium of the feminine and fill it with their presence."

She looked at him questionly.

"For a man, it feels like death to enter your woman, because you never know what is waiting there. There might be demons you might meet, and you have no clue whether they are yours or hers. In fact, you do not know and you will not be able to find out as you are becoming one with her. There is a lot of fear around this, as you can guess. It is the *unknown* that feels like death. Men want to avoid this. They either do not enter at all, or you get drunk beforehand—drunk with alcohol, pictures, images, scents, straps, anything which helps them to not experience the moment of this surrendering to death, anything to not be fully present."

He paused, then added solemnly, "It is the intent that makes the energy full and round and vibrant, my love; the intent to be fully present in the woman, with all her twists and turns, *knowing* that those twists and turns are mirrors of one's own emotions."

He looked deeply into her eyes.

"It is the intent. Everything is being manifested through the intent. If the intent is lacking, there is no true union. Same with love, Clara. If you are holding back your love, you will not experience the surrendering into your own wholeness."

9

INTO THE EARTH

"We should be grateful for the earth's magnetism," Clara said contemplatively.

"Pardon me?" Erna asked, irritated. "Where did this suddenly come from?"

They were standing in the queue at the cashier of the fast food restaurant with a tray of cheese and bread in front of them.

Clara ignored her question. "If there were no earthly magnetism, there would be nothing which keeps our feet to the ground. I wonder where the magnetic force derives from?"

"It might be a giant magnet in the center of the earth." Erna shrugged. "I have no idea." She moved her tray forward and scrutinized the various drinks that were offered. She did not seem to be overly interested in the subject.

"It could also be a black hole in her center," Clara said abruptly. She stared intensely at the neck of the woman in front of her. "A black hole like a caldera which continuously attempts to suck everything into its monstrous mouth—including us humans."

"Hmmm," Erna uttered, now searching for coins in her purse. "Seems to be a black hole in here, too. Not a very comforting thought, this."

"Imagine, the black hole is actually her shadow, or even better, her soulmate. Imagine that her magnetism is actually based on the force of attraction within her! It might be the beloved within who is calling her. It could be her attempt to come home and merge with her other part. We might feel their mutual attraction through the earth's magnetism. Wouldn't that make a lot of sense?"

Clara started dancing around. "Would that not explain the extraordinary force?" she shouted.

Erna looked at her with an inexplicable mixture of amusement and concern. "I can see how much you have grown into all this tantra stuff," she said. "I hope you do not go nuts." She threw a few coins on the tray.

"Can you not feel the pull?" Clara asked airily, spiralling around her own axis. "I can feel it!"

"Eight twenty-five," the woman at the register said.

"Are we sharing this, or do you want me to take this and you pay for breakfast tomorrow?" Erna asked with a stern face.

"If I stay with this vision of Earth endeavoring to return home and become one with her beloved, I can feel the pull within me," Clara said dreamily. She swirled around faster. "It is very sweet and very strong. It is as if I had moved into this caldera myself, and there is nothing I can do. I am irresistibly being pulled towards the very center of it. How magical this is. How wonderful and also irresistibly sweet."

Erna nodded reluctantly. She handed over the money to the sales assistant. Then she grabbed Clara's arm. "Come on, Clara. Let us talk about it at home, okay?"

Clara did not seem to notice Erna's pushing. "Can you not feel it?" she asked breathlessly.

"I admit, I do feel something. But why is it wonderful?"

"You resist the pull," Clara sang, still dancing around. "Do you notice how much you resist the pull?"

"I do not want to be devoured by some monster, even if it is the earth's lover himself," Erna muttered, picking up the tray.

"We are attracted by their attraction," Clara sang. She felt a flood of heat rushing up in her body. "We are going back into the earth, and from there into the beyond. We will be one with all. How does this sound?"

"I do not know," Erna said, shaking her head in disbelief, holding the tray tightly to herself. "I'd rather stick to the status quo, Clara. Thank you for the inspiration, my dear. Let's do something real now. Let's find a table and eat. Come on!" She kicked the tray into Clara's side.

"Okay." Clara gave in, sighing. "I am happy to have discovered this, whether you believe it or not. It for sure grounds me into this earth, making it somewhat more conscious and *attractive*, this magnetism."

"I can see that," Erna said, smiling suspiciously. Suddenly she pushed the tray into Clara's hands.

"Carrying our food is pretty grounding too, my friend. I would suggest you do it. Okay? See that table over there? Make a move! I am starving."

* * *

"Anubis, yesterday I meditated about Yeshe and Chenrezig again. Suddenly, pain stabbed me in my heart like a knife. I felt so abandoned by something I could only name as *the masculine*. It was not a specific man I was so desperately missing. It was the masculine qualities, or values, as I understand them from you. I did not know what to do with my pain, nor did I know what to focus upon to release it. It was terrible. I felt like an animal caught in a cage much too small for me."

Anubis's eyes turned dark. "When the feminine misses presence and a clear direction, it goes crazy," he said, sounding distressed.

"Then, all at once," Clara said, "an image of the earth floated up in my mind. It was as if I had slipped into this enormous womb of her where I downloaded my pain into her womb. It was such a relief. During the whole process, though, I knew that the masculine was still absent. I somehow got the impression that she, too, is in pain about being abandoned. Even Earth! How can this be? Did I make this up?" She moved her head to the sides as if she could shake off those emotional torrents raging wihin her.

"No," he said. "You did not make this up. You are part of the emotional pain-body of the earth. There is no separation between you, the earth, and all its residents."

"But why did it feel as if she is abandoned, too?" Clara cried out, clenching her fists.

"There is no true presence and direction by the ones who call themselves *rulers* of the earth."

"You mean *humanity*," Clara said and snivelled.

"Yes. Doesn't it say in your religious books, 'Fill the earth and subdue it; and have dominion over the fish of the sea and over the birds of the air and over every living thing that moves upon the earth?' There is not much love here in this saying. No love penetrating the earth to its core," Anubis added quietly.

"Most humans are not aware that they live on a truly miraculous planet. They do not understand that if there were no Earth, they would not be here either."

"Why was the pain so intense?"

"It was a wake-up call for your own masculine side within you to make itself known and take responsibility. Now you know it is important to stay present with the pain. By holding the space for it, you are also contributing to the healing of the emotional body of the earth."

She looked up in surprise.

"How can I heal the earth's pain?" she asked incredulously.

"You are one with the earth," Anubis answered. "All memories are saved in her emotional body. They are fields of consciousness with succinct vibrational levels. When you connect with them through your own experience—when you have the same vibration as those fields of consciousness—you feel the pain of abandonment on a much larger scale."

"I could hardly bear this pain. I do not know why I say *I*, because there was a *me*, and at the same time, there was no *me* anymore. At some point, something in me reached up and started praying for healing."

"By you opening to another vibration other than the one you experienced through her emotional body, you opened a space where healing energies came in."

He cast her a cautious look. "Continue witnessing her pain and let it enter your heart, my love. Only then can it move and dissolve in the presence of your love. This is the task you have taken on when incarnating on this earth. You are all tuning forks. You are all able to download higher vibrations through your bodies into the earth. The earth will be healed by your own healing. So it will be, ultimately, with every human being on this planet."

He reached out to her and gently stroked her arms.

"This is a lot of new information, Clara. It will sink into your awareness gradually. Trust the process, and relax into it. You can't do anything wrong here."

* * *

"He is never there," she whined. "Even if I were the enlightened feminine, he would not notice. There are about a hundred and fifty forest fires, so to speak, to look at and get under control in his life right now; that is how I feel it. His need to get new jobs as a film producer, his ex-wife, his grown-up kid! He has so much on his plate. He is never really with me. In his eyes I see only the distraction. I feel so lonely. And yet, I know that expressing my loneliness would just be another forest fire for him—fire site number one hundred fifty-one—which he would feel compelled to extinguish. He is never there. And I am stuck in my despair. How can we ever live together, Anubis? I have no idea."

"When you are drowning in your despair, and he is absent, you do not really meet," Anubis said dryly. "At least one of you must be present and in the sacred witness, even if it is painful. Otherwise, if there is too much identification with all these patterns, you will find it hard to shift the energy."

"Painful?" she screamed. "It is unbearable!"

The echo of her words rang in her ears. How pathetic, she thought at the same time.

He chuckled. "Come on. Don't be dramatic. Have you ever heard of drama leading you out of your story? No? On the contrary. It tends to suck you deeper into it." He stroked her arms soothingly. "And yet, I see you are in pain, so I want to acknowledge it."

"How can I raise my vibration?" she asked fervently. She felt a rush of heat in her face. "I am sick of being the poor cow."

"Poor cow?" he asked, amused.

"Suffering, I mean."

He looked at her soberly. "Practice being aware of him and of me as your Spirit Mate at the same time. You will notice that you will not be swamped by your emotions. You will be able to master them. Then you have the chance to become the very path for you both to walk together."

* * *

"We finally made love again this morning," Clara explained in a low voice.

"Oh!" Anubis said, smirking. "How come?"

"I have no idea," Clara answered. "I have no idea how we both got there. We realized, all our quarrelling did not make much sense. We pushed everything away, ignored our resistance, and went for it."

Clara was standing in a queue at the supermarket when he had turned up beside her. "You look so radiant today," he had whispered. "What happened?"

The surroundings seemed to be ablazed with light when she saw him.

"I am impressed," Anubis now said with a grin. "That was a huge step."

She felt herself blushing, then she laughed out loud. "Stop making fun of me, Anubis. You could be a bit jealous, no?"

"Oh, come on, Clara, you know that when you make love with me, you make love with the world. Same the other way around. When you make love with the world, you make love with me. We are all one, with the minor difference of meeting each other on different frequencies. It is your decision."

"How can I decide if I do not know about the higher frequencies?" Clara asked absent-mindedly while moving forward in the queue. The people around her did not seem to notice anything strange. Only a beautiful elderly woman with long, white hair at the other end of the queue had suddenly looked at her attentively.

Clara handed over a 10-Euro note to the cashier.

"Since the beginning of your life, there were glimpses around you reminding you of those other realities," Anubis answered. "Some people see them as sparks of light. Others just feel them. As a child, just looking at a flower made you blissful. You knew how to drink its color, how to become one with it. Remember, you constantly experience many more frequencies than your mind can grasp. You must set your intent, though. The rest will follow. But let us get back to you and Marco. How did it happen?"

Clara shrugged and shoved her purchases into her bag. "We met again, and it was as if we both had pushed a switch to *go*."

Anubis scrutinized her. "Did you enjoy it?"

"It wasn't as if it was the big gift! I kind of thought, well, why not? I felt a bit numb."

"Sounds as if you were afraid," Anubis said. "You were afraid that there might be some disappointment lurking around the corner. That numb state of yours is a fake state. Numbness will not help you move through the pain. Still, it is great that you did not follow its calling."

"It was not easy," she said, taking her bag and moving towards the supermarket exit. When she stood in the blazing sun of the late autumn day, she murmured, "I was somewhat open to him." She looked away with a guilty expression on her face.

"What is up?" he asked and put his arm around her. "Can I help you with your bag, by the way?"

She laughed. "No, thank you, Anubis," she said. "You do not really want other people to wonder about my bag floating in the air, do you?"

He joined her laughter. "No," he said, "but what about changing the weight of it?"

Clara suddenly felt her bag moving up in the air beside her. Her hands still held it, but it seemed to have suddenly gotten a mind of its own. Nervously, she tore it down so that it stayed in its original place. "Anubis!" she hissed. "Stop that!"

A nearby man looked towards her with an expression of surprise on his face.

"Talking out loud might create more attention," she heard

Anubis saying. He slowly raised his arms and touched her at her shoulders. "Now you are closing down, Clara. Your heart is pounding heavily. What a turmoil you are in!"

"I felt quite a bit of resistance this morning," she said wretchedly. "Even though I had been struggling for this to happen so long, I could not help feeling resistance."

"What did you do?"

She felt her face starting to glow. Then she giggled. "I connected with you. Then I felt guilty. Did I deceive him with you? Am I like one of those people who lose themselves by fantasizing about hot sex?"

"What happened then?" Anubis asked, ignoring her question. His face held a curious expression.

Clara opened the back of her car and dropped off her bag. Then she slammed the door with a bang and dropped herself onto the driver's seat. Closing her door, she mumbled, "There was an immediate rush of energy streaming into me. It was as if my whole body lit up. I felt your presence everywhere—from the tip of my toes to my crest, all the way down my arms, into my fingers, and quite strongly in—"

"In your beautiful breasts and nipples," he added with a tender look on his face, making himself comfortable next to her.

She nodded. "Yes," she then said simply.

"It is your kundalini energy saying hello to you. I guess it made quite a difference in your lovemaking," Anubis said.

"It did indeed," Clara exclaimed. "It changed the whole energy. It was as if we were both being uplifted. Each movement of our bodies created so much more bliss. When he touched my skin, it was so exquisite, and indeed, nearly unbearable in its intensity."

She quivered at the thought of it.

"He experienced it as well. We both enjoyed so much being

together like that."

"You increased your vibration by connecting with a higher vibration within you, and he moved with you," Anubis stated crisply. "Great experience, isn't it? It is also called *quickening*. It also works vice versa."

"What do you mean?"

"Imagine you feel low, and he connects with his inner woman, his very own goddess, whom he worships and surrenders to; you would also immediately feel the shift in the vibration."

Clara was dumbfounded. "I never thought about that!" She shook her head. "So you do not think I deceived him with you?"

"Have you ever read about those ancient Egyptian mummification rituals?" Anubis asked.

"No. What were they about?"

"In Egypt, every part of the body was dedicated to a god or a goddess. There was the belief that the body was a temple, the home of all the divine beings in the Egyptian realm. The Egyptians would say, 'My hair is the hair of Nut, my eyes are the eyes of Hathor, my face is the face of Ra, my ears and lips are the ears and lips of Anubis, my womb is the womb of Isis,' and so on. So in a way, you applied those ancient customs, with the minor difference that you chose only me instead of the whole pantheon."

Anubis smiled. "I do not mind that at all," he added with a broad grin on his face. He indicated for her to head off in the direction of her apartment.

"Let's go home," he said.

* * *

"I am confused, Anubis."

"What is up, my love?" he asked.

"You know," she said and hesitated, "making love with Marco yesterday was very strange. I did not want to do it for myself, so for whom, then? It was as if I could see and feel how much ego there could be in just *going* for it, whether spiritually, or tantrically, or *the normal way*. It was so very strange to do the lovemaking without attachment. It was really intense, though. When I focused on my heart, the pleasure deepened. When I concentrated on heightening my sensations and building up momentum, the pleasure decreased."

Anubis looked at her thoughtfully. "Whenever there is willforce, there is contraction," he then said. "The energy is being suppressed. When you imagine your heart as an ever-opening flower petal, you will notice how much more you are ready to surrender."

His gaze became more intense. "It is a surrender to the opening of your heart petal, rather than to another human being, Clara. It feels somewhat impersonal, because the usual emotional *hocus-pocus* and physical excitement does not take place. You, in fact, do not surrender to him, but to the opening space. It is an endless opening and surrendering. It is the feminine path towards enlightenment."

"But how do I open endlessly?" Clara asked incredulously. "I am far too afraid to do this!"

He nodded appreciatively. "There is the calling, right at this point. It is the calling for the enlightened masculine within you to join you with its presence and pure yang power to fully penetrate all the emotions which are there, and do not—I repeat, *not*—shrink back. If the two merge, you will stay in control, as the sacred witness. You will be in total control, because with the realized masculine principle within yourself, you will be able to hold all the contradictions within yourself."

He looked at her attentively to see whether she understood.

"Both the woman, as well as the man, will feel their fear, their pain, rage, and sadness, and you will still be able to nourish the openness to all that is. You are becoming open to all of existence. You are starting to embrace everything."

He smiled. "That is the blessing of the union of the enlightened masculine and feminine qualities, both in a man and in a woman. When you are on this path, your familiar approach regarding lovemaking will shift. You will feel strangely detached for a while. It is an unknown state. You will be reaching the other side. I can so much see you there, Clara. You do not know how much I am in awe of you for walking this path."

* * *

Rage fueled her. There was a hurricane within her, making her tremble like a volcano ready to burst. Yet she would contain it. She swore to herself she would contain it. She would not utter a word. If Marco decided to stay in his victimhood, she swore to herself, whatever he will do, she will contain her energy and let herself be completely burnt up by her rage, in the hope that an alchemical process will change her into something similar to gold and not only cold ashes.

"Where the hell are you?" she shouted out, this time to Aunubis. There was no response.

She would not usher a tone, would not spill out even a tiny bit of energy. Instead, she would use all her energy to burn herself up, completely. Ho!

With that last silent exclamation, something in her calmed. A decision had been made.

"Why are you so angry?" she suddenly heard Anubis asking.

Relieved, she dropped her shoulders. "Where were you?" she mumbled, her voice betraying anger.

"My sweetheart, you need to be a little bit more receptive. How will you experience me inside you if you are out there somewhere, taken away by your rage?"

She was silent.

"Do you grant him the right to feel like a victim?" he asked.

"All his hostility is based on him feeling like a victim," she responded sharply. "I cannot stay quiet in the face of his attempts to hurt me."

"You are right, my love. His patterns are coming up to the surface, aren't they? As well as yours. You are mirrors to each other, perfect mirrors. He mirrors to you what you mirror to him."

"I can see that," she said after a moment. "This is a big one, for heaven's sake, I can see that." She exhaled deeply.

"You are now taking charge of your feelings, do you notice this, Clara? Your rage was your expression of your own victimhood."

"Do you want to know what our dispute was about?" Clara asked.

"No." Anubis shook his head. "It is not important. Stories are never that important. The emotions wrapped in them are. They need to be fully felt and released. What about doing something useful, my love? What about some more tantric exercise? What do you reckon?"

* * *

When I closed my eyes and drifted away into the dreamtime, I saw a milky-white snake winding herself around the solid trunk of a tree. I knew it was me who was the snake, because I can still feel those meandering movements within my body. He was the trunk, a trunk with branches and dark green leaves. There was a slithering and rubbing of skin to skin, or was it skin to bark? I do not know, but my body knows. My body remembers the sensation, the roughness of the touch and the subsequent sweetness of melting in the heat. Although it was an airy experience, my body remembers. I tell you, my body remembers.

When we became one, the only image I was able to hold on to was a blazing fire, a fire extinguishing all my forms, all his forms, all forms, and there was nothing left, just the red-hot flames of the fire and me being a spark in it, together with him, one with the flames.

Then, my tears came. It felt as if I had suddenly dropped into another depth of my longing, of my belonging, and thus of my wholeness within. There was a decision surging up to the surface of my consciousness. I would not let myself be taken away by the longing. I would always remember how it feels to be one. I understood that the longing itself leads me away from the experience of my wholeness within. It is a romance, and it is an illusion.

My tears washed away the debris. They left me soft and raw on the inside. They were gentle, and at the same time passionate, as they connected me to my truth within. This must be the sacred union many mystics talk about. If they do. Maybe many of them turned mute.

The mystery has lifted its veil for a split second. I feel very blessed.

10

COMPLETING THIS CIRCLE

When her grandmother died over twenty years after her grandpa, the nurse had tried to console Clara by saying that it had been a peaceful death.

"In a way," the nurse had added, "death is always a celebration, except when it is sudden or violent. Except in the case of accidents or suicides," she had added. Then she turned round to leave the hospital room.

Clara stood there, motionless and grief-stricken. All of a sudden, she saw her grandparents' home, the house how it had been thirty years ago when her grandfather had died in the adjacent garden.

Except in the case of accidents or suicides, she thought, disconsolate as she closed her eyes.

She suddenly knew he was still there. That he had still not found the way into the light. That he was lost between the worlds, not really here nor there, still shocked by his accident, the turmoil, the people in the hospital, and then the final switch-off of the life-guarding machines which had stopped his physical life on this earth.

"Wrap the house with light," Anubis said, but she already knew what she had to do. In her imagination, she put up a giant pyramid with a crystal top around the house, and a second one upside down with an equal top into the earth.

Then she held the image of light streaming up and down from the two crystal tops, radiating out into the universe and towards the center of the earth, then flowing back into the pyramids and the house.

It was easy for her to hold up this image. The energy was stable, and she also had the impression that there was invisible support around her for her to keep up the image of the pyramids around the house.

Suddenly, she felt a rush of thankfulness. "If it were not you," she whispered to her grandfather, "I would not have been here. Thank you."

Deep love filled her at that moment. It surprised her. She had never been aware of a profound fondness for her grandpa. He had always been a distant person, a person to be respected, a person who smiled when he gave her sweets once in a while. Now there was a connection, a true connection on another level. It was as if a part of her had been lost and had returned. It had found its right place within her. Somehow, a space had opened up. She envisioned him moving into that space to find his way home into the light. A wave of peace surged within her.

When she opened her eyes, she knew that something had come to a peaceful end. She felt whole. Now, all was good.

* * *

"The circle reached its completion," Anubis said and lit a match. They stood outside in the dark, at the northern most rim of the Alps, one of her favourite spots in the forest. He had asked her to help him gather firewood. It was easy to find dry sticks, as it had not been raining for weeks. There was a fireplace in the middle of the clearing. It was dimly lit by the moonlight, a half moon hanging solemnly up in the sky, occasionally covered by misty clouds. Quietly they collected the material, and within a short time, they had built a little pyramid of wood. It would burn well.

"You went through your own underworld, and you will do it again and again," Anubis said while watching the fire springing over from the match to the dry branches. "It is the eternal progress of all beings, the moving in circles along the spiral towards an ever higher and higher consciousness. You have completed another cycle of your journey. It is time to celebrate, my love."

The fire began to crackle, and soon flames leapt into the sky. Clara stared into the red flames. She felt their heat in her face. Yes, she realized that something had come to an end. She had moved from a perception of her being in the world as a separate and dissociated self towards a reality of connectedness and love. This process, really, was a discovery of her own power. No longer did she see herself as a victim of circumstances. Now that she had grasped another reality underneath the physical world, she understood that creation and Creator were one and that she lived in a holographic reality. A shift on the inside would immediately create a shift on the outside. What she focused upon made all the difference, whether it be the light or the dark. It was up to her to decide anew every minute. She took a deep breath.

Anubis rustled in his pocket and took out a small package. He unwrapped it, and when the moonlight fell on it, Clara gasped. It was a sparkling ruby set in a medieval-style oval apron made of silver.

"This crystal shall remind you of the treasures you have found on your journey towards enlightenment. When you feel discouraged or disoriented, look at the crystal and know of the quantum leaps you have made in those last months. This cycle has come to an end, and it is a new beginning, like the Uruborus, the mythical serpent. For now, my beloved, we rest in that space between the ending and the beginning and celebrate. Let us do ceremony."

He reached for his bag and took out a blanket. When he stretched it out on the forest floor, Clara held her breath. There were small silver stars stitched in a circle on the dark velvety material, and they glistened in the moonlight. They were mirroring the light of the stars in the night sky. The fire crackled and shot orange sparks into the air.

Anubis came around to her and gently wrapped her in the blanket. "My star woman," he said, holding her in his arms and kissing her softly on her mouth.

When she opened herself to him, she knew the night sky would pour its stars into her and that she, herself, would become part of the night sky.

* * *

She slipped down the stairs into that cave buried deep within herself. Anubis had told her to go ahead. He would follow in a moment, and they would meet at the lake.

It has been a long time since I walked down these stairs, she thought, excitement and trepidation rising within her. It was dark and wet everywhere, and water dripped on the stairs, her head, and her clothes. She shivered.

Next time, I will bring my raincoat and an umbrella, she thought half-desperately, half-amused. I mean, can you believe it? I go into my own underworld, and it is dripping wet? Where is the light, anyway? Seems as if someone has decided to dim it down. I can hardly see anything.

Ouch!

She slipped and nearly toppled to the ground. Only at the last moment did she regain her equilibrium by gripping some rocks at her left side. Her skin burned from being scratched. A thick liquid slowly moved down her hand. She held her hand in front of her eyes, but in the dim light, she could not see much, only a dark trail moving down her skin.

"Damn," she said. The echo of her voice reverberated in the air. She licked her hand, and the metallic taste of blood filled her mouth. The familiarity of it calmed her. Gradually, the wound stopped bleeding. It did not seem to be a big scratch.

Why does it take so long to reach the bottom, she wondered. It had never before taken so long! I must have descended at least a hundred steps. Where the hell am I going?

Suddenly she felt something moving rapidly towards her right side. Each tiny hair of her body rose in anticipation. A wild and vigorous flapping of wings stirred the air, and with a high-pitched sound, an animal soared out of the dark. It nearly dashed into her face, but only within a breath away, it made a turn, and with a final flap of the wings, it glided back away into the dark.

She stood, horrified.

What was that? she thought, her eyes piercing through the blackness. There was nothing to see, only the sound of dripping water which continued to crawl into her ears like an eternal torturing noise.

She was alone. Even the stairs below her had vanished into the dark.

Panic crawled up her spine, filling her with an overwhelming feeling of powerlessness and terror. Her hands and feet grew numb.

I know this feeling, she thought with rising horror. I need to get out of it. How can I possibly get out of this? Thoughts criss-crossed through her head backwards and forwards; what is there to do? Is there a threat? Am I in danger? Will there be another attack? She shuddered and felt her hands becoming sweaty.

She felt close to fainting. "No, I will not!" she said out loud, her voice cracking. She knew that only her willpower would help her survive this. There was a tiny space opening in her consciousness, allowing her to observe how her mind anxiously tried to find the most appropriate reaction to this. There was no escape. Her mind did not know what to do, and she had no idea, either. She would be completely lost in this state of immobility and horror, stuck between two worlds on those stairways between her home and her underworld. Her mind went bleak.

Suddenly she remembered Anubis saying, *if you freeze, move! Force yourself to move. It does not matter where to and why—the movement itself is the key for your body to release the shock pattern.*

With a conscious and vigorous shake of her arms, she broke the unspoken spell. She threw her arms high up into the air, rolled her head backwards and forwards, and made her legs shiver. Then she jumped up and down, as much as the slippery condition of the stairs allowed her to do.

Ahhh, she thought, this is so good. Still, one part of her remained terrified, but although that part weakened her, it did not have as much power over her. This is so good, she thought again, jumping up and down.

Come on, Clara, you can make it, come on! She cheered herself on, and although she did not know what for, her body relaxed.

When she came to a halt, she heard herself breathing heavily. The image of the winged creature which had nearly hit her face popped up in her head.

It must have been a bat, she suddenly realized.

Then she laughed loudly.

Well, if it was a bat, she wanted to say hello to me! She remembered the dream meditation when she had met this power animal of hers for the first time. Later, she had read about bats—how they send out sounds which bounce off objects and produce echoes they can hear and interpret. This is how they moved around in the darkness.

She wants me to move around in darkness without being hurt or injured, she thought. Thank you for reminding me, little bat. I will now be tuning into your amazing animal capabilities as I continue my walk. Her shoulders dropped in relief.

"Could you teach me how to move safely in this darkness," she said in a choked voice. "Please," she added in a begging tone.

Then she remembered Anubis telling her that she would never find anything which was not already within her. What did he mean by that? Should she try and connect with the animal on an inner plane, rather than looking for it somewhere out there? Should she imagine this bat to be in her body? As soon as she finished the thought, she felt a stirring in her chest. Was there something moving within her? Did it feel like the flapping of wings?

"This is awesome!" she thought.

"Are you there?" she asked. Then she remembered the picture of the bat in her apartment. The bat was hanging from the ceiling, motionless and calm. The moment she fixed that image in her head, Clara relaxed. No need to do anything, she thought with relief. One lesson of the bat is to just hang out there and rest and wait for an impulse from within to move. The bat is in complete trust, she noticed with surprise. The bat's state of being is a state of complete and wholesome trust.

She sighed deeply. The thought had soothed her.

Slowly she continued her walk down the stairs. The light remained dim, but when she focused her attention on the presence in her chest, she became more trusting. Then, after what seemed to be an endless walk, she reached the last step.

"Finally," she said loudly. "Finally, I have arrived at some sort of a bottom."

The lake laid in front of her in shades of gray and blue. There were no movements to be seen, not even waves of water rippling against the shore. The silence was omnipresent.

She sat down and picked up a pebble. It lay heavy in her palm.

Slowly she turned it with her fingers and enjoyed the cool, smooth texture of it. Then, all of a sudden, she threw the pebble far across the water. The pebble disappeared beneath the surface without a further trace.

Clara looked up. Only now did she notice the gathering of giant dark clouds above her.

Where is the cave ceiling? As soon as the question arose in her mind, the rumble of a faraway thunderstorm sounded in her ears. She jumped up and screened the horizon.

With rising anticipation, she wondered where the noise came from. Again, thunder rolled through the air. It seemed to be coming from everywhere, echoing from all the walls of the cave which were not visible to her, hidden beneath an ominous kind of fog. The thundering noise grew louder, and whilst she could see flashes of lightning high above her, she suddenly felt the earth trembling beneath her.

"Oh no!" she gasped with rising horror. A crack formed right beside her feet as the earth surface broke open with a groaning that sounded entirely inhuman. She watched the crack moving along an invisible line, revealing an impenetrable darkness at its edges, a darkness which had neither a beginning nor end. There was nothing below the earth's surface, no visible earthen substance, no stones or clay, just pitch-black darkness widening into an ever-bigger abyss. She stared at the opening in terror. At the same time, stones tumbled down, heavy stones thudding against the ground—first only a few, then rocks over rocks hitting the ground, an avalanche of rocks, inexorably, in a terrifying cacophony of sounds.

She felt enormous pressure in her body, a magnetic force trying to pull her into the abyss as rocks fell from above. This cave will implode, she thought. I will be buried alive in this place, and nobody will know where I am.

The lake's waves grew higher and higher. They crashed against the shore with increasing violence. She stood there transfixed, motionless.

Suddenly she heard his voice. "Move, my beloved, move," he whispered. "Move into the tiny spaces of your cells, move into the light within your body, move. It is the only way out of this state of being you are in, my beloved. Move. You must shift into the essence of your being, and connect with the light within. Now, Clara, move. Otherwise, it will be too late."

She clearly heard his words, but she did not grasp their meaning. Her mind had frozen. She could not think a single thought; the only thing she could perceive was the ever-widening crack beneath her feet radiating a magnetic force which she could hardly bear.

Again, she heard him whisper, "Please, Clara, go within. Do not fall for the illusions of this world; go within."

Suddenly she felt a familiar flap of wings at her cheek. A dark shadow had appeared in her right periphery, gliding through the air with a high-pitched sound. She shuddered. The bat! Was she trying to push her out of her state of immobility?

"Move within," Anubis said again in her head, and this time, she obeyed.

She closed her eyes, and started to search for the light within her body. With surprise she noticed that its magnificent and crystal-clear brilliance was already everywhere. It seemed to move like ebb and flow within her, radiating from each tiny little space in each of her cells. It even expanded through her skin to the outside. Intuitively, she knew there was another body of hers, a luminous, eclipse-shaped light, vibrating in ever-widening circles and in more and more diverse colors. The white-diamond light broke into all of the rainbow colors, and with a sudden movement, she stretched out her arms as if she had wings. She threw back her head, shoved her feet against the ground, and lifted that new body of hers through the rocks and the gaps of the tectonic plates of the earth, into the air and out into space, a space filled with a sparkling night sky. She found herself utterly free, and with a ferocious and triumphant roaring sound, she threw herself high up into the night sky.

* * *

"Clara, Clara, are you okay? Please, Clara, please wake up."

Someone softly touched Clara's arm, then shook it more vigorously. With effort, she opened her eyes.

Erna had switched on the lights. She sat upright in the bed and looked down at Clara, a deeply perturbed expression on her face. "Are you okay?" she asked again. "You were quivering, as if electric jolts went through you. I am really worried!"

Clara looked into Erna's face. She raised her hand and gently stroked her friend's cheek. Then she began to laugh. At the same time, tears stung her eyes. "You know," she whispered through her laughing and crying, "you know I just survived my own death." When she saw Erna's startled look, she laughed even more.

"Do not worry," she said. "I am not hysterical. I just had the most amazing dream. You know what? When we die, there is only light. That is all there is. The light within us is the light that lives forever. Isn't that comforting?" Another bout of laughter rolled through her body.

Then she closed her eyes again. Her body relaxed. Erna put her arms around her and rocked her like a little child.

"You are so good to me," Clara murmured. "Thank you so much." With those words, she fell asleep again.

* * *

"It is a bit embarrassing," Clara said, heat rising in her face. "I mean, there is part of me which totally surrenders to him, which gives myself entirely to him. Bowing down to him and telling him he is my master is really quite something, isn't it? I mean, I am a modern woman after all, with a solid education of feminist thinking and so on. But here I am, lying at his feet, at least theoretically, worshipping him as my master. Uumph." She stamped her feet to shake off some of the snowflakes on her coat and bonnet.

Erna grinned and shrugged. She seemed to be enjoying herself. She tap danced around clumsily with her winter boots while grimacing like a spoilt girl. The two women were on their way towards the main square of the city. Every other moment, they sidestepped one of the cyclists who had been courageous enough to hop on their bikes in this weather. The snow fell in big, fluffy flakes that silently floated through the air. Slowly and obliviously, they covered all surfaces with their innocent white.

"Well," Erna said with a deep and preaching voice, "you are not lost, my sister, as long as there is this sacred witness in you . . . as long as this witness is aware of everything and takes notes. You will always be able to rise up like Lazarus and leave, if you have switched on your mode to the sacred witness."

"Oh, yes," Clara said warily. This was for sure the beginning of one of Erna's monologues. She straightened up. Well, if Erna is heading off, she thought, I'd better get her out of her teacher's role right now.

"Oh yes," Clara repeated with more vigor, and she began to prance around as well. "My beloved sacred witness, hello? Are you there? Oh no!" She then gasped melodramatically. "You fell asleep, and here you are, snoring like a villain, oh my precious goddess. What can I do? What can I do?"

Clara had fallen into a sing-song melody and spread her arms. She lifted her head and looked up into the sky.

Then she held her breath. The sight was awesome. There were snowflakes everywhere, millions and millions of snowflakes whirling above her. The sheer amount of flakes falling from the sky made her speechless. A very different reality had moved into her awareness; it had found an opening within her and captured her entire being. It was a reality deprived of sounds. It was a reality full of swirling white, fluffy snowflakes. This new reality was vast and mysterious. It had no boundaries. It seemed to stretch into eternal space. It was dizzying. It seemed to pervade everything with stillness.

Where do you all come from? she wondered as she stared into the array of tumbling flakes. She closed her eyes. Would she be able to decode the secret patterns behind the snowflakes' whirling dance? Could she pierce through this impenetrable veil and find the hidden truth? At that moment, her vision blurred. She became aware of the space above her, the space between the surface of her upturned face and those invisible clouds hovering high above those whirling white flakes. She felt airy and vast, as if she herself had no boundaries.

Those flakes fall all the way from the heavens, she thought with childlike delight.

Some of those flakes touched her face and melted. Trickles of water started to roll down the sides of her neck.

"They are surrendering to me," she muttered to herself. "Those snowflakes that fall on my face, they surrender to my warm skin. Parts of them evaporate into the air, and parts of them move into my skin and merge with the liquids in my cells. Do they inform me of the essence of their being? Do they keep their crystal structure? Are they imprinting mine or merging with mine?"

She saw the entire weather cycle the snowflakes were part of— the rivers and oceans, the rising of the water as steam, the gathering and cooling down in the clouds, and again the falling. While the snowflakes melted on her skin, she realised in amazement how much she, herself, was part of the cycle, too. The water in her cells had also been part of the clouds, the rivers, the oceans.

There was an impulse within her to wipe away the moisture, but she resisted it. She wanted to succumb to the sensation of the cool liquid running down her skin. It was so exquisite, so sensual. She shivered. When her neck started to ache from the stretch, she lowered her head and turned to Erna.

Erna had witnessed her face expression change. "What is up?"

Then she waved her hands. Without waiting for an answer, she said in a serious voice, "I can think of at least four cherished women who gave their lives for that energy of surrender to the divine. Still nowadays, they are being worshipped for their deep devotion."

Here I am, back again in noisy Munich, Clara thought, bewildered and amused at the same time. She licked her lips. Some of the snowflakes had just landed there. They tasted fresh and cool. Hello, messengers from an airy white and strange world.

"Do you want to know who those women are?" Erna asked with an impatient trace in her voice.

"Sure," Clara answered, sticking out her tongue. It seemed the easiest answer at that moment. In truth, she did not care. She tried to catch a few snowflakes on her tongue without much success.

"One was Teresa of Avila," Erna said, looking at her suspiciously. "She had a mystical experience of feeling her heart pierced with rapturous love by an angel. Her poetry is awesome. Want some lines?"

Without waiting for Clara to answer, she proclaimed,

"Already I gave myself completely,

and have changed in such a way

That my Beloved is for me

and I am for my Beloved."

She stopped, then scrutinized Clara to see the effects of her words. Then she added in an explanatory tone, "You see, Teresa of Avila addressed this angel being, and she also called him beloved."

"Those lines are intimate," Clara said dreamily.

"Yes!" Erna said. "They are, indeed. So what?"

"Well, nothing," Clara answered vaguely. She could not figure out where Erna was heading to.

"There is a wonderful, but also pretty controversial erotic sculpture of Teresa. The artist was the famous sculptor Bernini. He earned much criticism for his alleged sexualized imagery. But you know what, Clara?" Erna bounced up and down.

"I do not care about the condemnation of eroticism in divine surrender. How much more desirable is it to surrender to an enlightened divine being and experience erotic ecstasies of surrendering to such an energy than to any of those half-conscious men or even sadomasochistic guys. Who claims that the erotic energy is an energy of the devil and not of the divine? Of God or the goddess, or Shiva and Shakti, you name it?"

Now Erna had a fiery look on her face. "Is there a good and a devilish ecstatic life energy?" she hollered.

"It can't be," Clara replied. "I tell you, this surrendering energy to the divine jars us entirely into another place. We women intuitively know of this gateway to heaven. We all yearn to surrender. Anubis would probably say the feminine part in men, too.

"But who to?" Erna asked and threw her arms into the air. "Do you want to surrender to a jerk who is demonstrating his superiority by beating you up?"

People were starting to turn their heads towards the two women.

"Please, Erna, will you stop pretending to be on stage! Will you please calm down?" Clara said. She dragged Erna by her coat. "Otherwise, someone might come up to us and inquire as to who is beating us up."

Erna looked at her. Then she started laughing. "Okay," she said, "I got your point. But did you get mine, too?"

Clara nodded and smiled faintly. "I am totally convinced," she said. "You are great. Are there more women like Teresa?"

"There are not only women, also men," Erna retorted. "My favourite poet, however, is Lal Ded. She is a great woman poet from Kashmir, and she is still being worshipped as a saint. Listen to this:

"I, Lalla, entered through the door of the garden of my mind

And saw Shiva and Shakti united into one, O joy!

I diffused outside the light that lit-up within me

And in that darkness I seized Him and held Him tight.

I awakened the Beloved

And by becoming one with Him

my mind and body became pure . . ."

"Why do you know all those lines by heart?" Clara asked. She was truly astonished. She had never seen this side of Erna.

"I have recently started to collect poems of the mystics of this world," Erna said. "I am fascinated by them. They express such an extraordinary surrender to the divine." She clasped her hands firmly together. "I cannot recall one experience in my life as deep as theirs." Turning to Clara, she said vehemently, "I do wonder if there is something fundamentally missing in my life, something very magical and ecstatic. I feel like an explorer heading out into an entirely unknown territory. You seem to feel the same, though you are taking a different route. We are both explorers. We are both drawn to the mystery."

Clara looked at her questionly. "Will you tell me about the men, too?"

"I will be delighted," Erna said. "Promise me, though, that you will never feel embarrassed again in that context, will you? Your devotion for Anubis is of a similar quality as the devotion of those poetesses to their beloveds. At least in my view. I quite frankly think you are blessed to be experiencing this, Clara."

Then Erna giggled. "You might become one of those devotional poets yourself. Goddess beware. Wouldn't that be wonderful?"

When Erna saw Clara's incredulous expression, she laughed. "Come on," she said, "let's do some goddess shopping. Let's get dressed for the 'real event'—whatever that might be. Maybe it will come up sooner than we pray for."

* * *

I finally came home.

Did I know why I was gone? Did I know what I was looking for?

My search was desperate.

I was frantic.

I was frantically looking for something I had no idea about. Frantically looking. Crazy woman I was. Depressed woman. Woman out of her wits. Two-hundred years ago, in Victorian times, I would have been called "the mad woman in the attic." In modern times, they have other terms: "attention-deficit-syndrome." Or the "borderline syndrome." Just the words make the ground below my feet tremble. I see myself balancing on a rocky ledge, like the one I visited last year with Erna, in the mountains near Munich. To my right, the rocks, dropping steeply into the valley, so steeply. To my left, the same. A narrow trail. Borderline. And my body so tight.

But my search was more than this shaky and tight feeling of walking on that trail high up above the valleys.

There was a ferocious movement forward, a pushing and pulling into the unknown, constantly, relentlessly, and sometimes quite exhausting! All the time, I felt the resistance to the dropping. To the endless dropping.

What was I so desperately looking for?

Now I know.

I recognized it when I found it.

I wanted to come home.

* * *

"Where is home?" Erna would ask.

"It is in the heart," I would answer. "Quite simply, in the heart."

* * *

Now I am hanging here, within my heart. Finally. Hanging like a bat. In the center of my home. My falling has stopped. There was a hook. And here at this hook, hooked into the center of myself, I hang. Completely relaxed.

Finally, I have found my ground.

Finally, I came home.

EPILOGUE

"It is not easy!" Erna said willfully. "You just wrote this. I tell you, it is not easy to be in the heart. Bullshit!"

"You are angry," Clara said, astounded.

"Of course I am angry," Erna yelled. "It is all that blah-blah new-age thing."

"Come on, let us try it," Clara said calmly. "Right now. Apparently, we do not need to wait for a specific moment in time. It can be done whenever."

I love my friend, she contemplated. *How good it is to know that there is so much love around and within us. We sometimes forget. But we have friends and partners and animals and light beings and the whole world to remind us that there is a lot of love in those in-between spaces.*

She remembered Anubis telling her to share her experiences.

"No excuses," he had said with a serious tone in his voice. "No excuses, Clara. Go back into your world, and share them in any way you can imagine."

"What for?" she had asked, her voice trailing away. She had buried her head in her coat. The boat underneath her had started to swing to both sides.

He did not respond. When she looked up again, he was gazing at the horizon where a faint pink light had appeared. She sighed.

"What for?" she asked again, although she knew the answer in advance.

"There are many caves down here," he had answered slowly. "Most of them deserted. People are afraid of visiting their underworld. You know that there is much to gain by it. It is in those in-between spaces where you find so much love. No one will pass the needle's eye who has not gone through their underworld and come up again. No one's heart will be as light as the feather of Ma'at if the heart's pain is still awaiting the embrace of awareness and its subsequent transformation into love."

He paused, then he said, "You know that you are not alone in this. Others don't. You need to tell them. You need to talk about the holographic realities of your consciousness. There are many gateways to the underworlds. When you began to trust your shaman sound healer, he paved the way for you to meet me. It only takes a hair-width of trust to let trust fully in. Again and again. A tiny opening can crack the most powerful rock. You need to talk about this."

His voice grew more pressing. "People will follow your trail until they come to a crossroad and start walking their own individual paths. As you did and still do. You are all following trails being created by the ones who walked before you. You stand at a crossroad, and then your choose your own path towards mastership. This is how you learn to walk your path with dignity, and grace, and serenity."

He fell silent for a moment.

"Talk about your path, Clara. Don't let yourself be victimized again. We are through this now. It is time to move on with your own sword of truth in one hand and the grail filled with your knowledge in the other. You are ready for it. Go."

The pink light had immersed vast parts of the horizon with its luminous essence. A new day was breaking. Clara stood, and with a resolute step, she jumped from the boat to the land. She walked across the empty plain to the staircase at the other side. When she reached it, she turned around. "Will you be there when I come back?" she called.

"I am always there. I am one with you," he answered quietly and smiled.

She hesitated, then she raised her arms to wave goodbye. She watched him moving away from the shore, a dark figure with his face covered in a black cape. He disappeared in a white sparkling mist which had suddenly risen upon the surface of the lake. It was an illusion. She knew she would never be alone again.

"Thank you," she said quietly. Then she went up the stairs and back into her world.

THE END

A NOTE FROM THE AUTHOR

I had been attracted by the dance of words since the age of twelve, when I interpreted my first school poem. I remember the poem was about a tree which grew in a house and broke through the roof. My body still holds the memory of this poem. Alas, I have no idea who the poet was. It took me decades to take my writing more seriously. In 2010, I joined the *The Writing Spirit School* by Lynn Andrews, author of over twenty books on the teachings of an amazing group of forty-four shaman women from all over the world—the Sisters of The Sisterhood of the Shields.

I had been reading Lynn's books for many years. They were so precious to me that I only read one or two a year, sparing them for the times to come. In those years, my own writing was stuck. Heaps of journal paper, a half-finished novel (in German), some short stories, some ideas for children books—all waited patiently for the big finish.

I discovered Lynn's School by sheer accident, or shall we say, by one of those synchronistic events which suddenly emerge out of the fog of existence and shed light on a crossroad ahead. After a tiring analysis of hundreds of curricula on creative writing courses, I followed an impulse to call up her website. There she was, announcing her first course of her school starting in a week's time.

Although I had by then read nearly all her books, I was little prepared for the turbulent shamanic journey ahead. More than once, I was catapulted out of my comfort zone. Mildly put, I experienced what shamans call *quickening*. With each new assignment, another horizon opened up, and I was called to evolve without much time to reflect. I often hesitated and scolded. To put it bluntly, I was dead afraid. Many times I woke up at night to fight those monsters who drastically demonstrated to me what it means to set out to new and unknown worlds. They proved excellent in using vivid imagery. They were unmistakably transparent about all the danger involved.

And I was a rewarding victim. I had heaps of fear within me.

I still have fear, but it has changed somehow. My fears became familiar to me, and at times now, I even shake my head and laugh about them. I see them as good enemies, or alternatively, grumpy acquaintances who join me on my journeys, waiting for an opportunity to give me a little push so that I stumble and drop out of my center of power. At times, this push is really painful, but on the whole, we are now playing hide-and-seek more often than the emotional tsunami game.

Unsurprisingly, each step across the borderline of my comfort zone was worth it. It still is. I have not reached any safe haven yet, and it has gradually dawned on me that I most likely never will. I was, however, graciously allowed to learn that one can stabilize oneself again and again in a challenging environment—as challenging as planet Earth can be for its human (and other) inhabitants.

When Lynn told me at one of the group phone-call sessions somewhere in the middle of her course, "Write a dialogue!" I was not amused, to say the least.

I had been a diligent apprentice; I had worked through the handbook and completed the assignments, no matter how irrational they had deemed me to be. I had progressed with the lessons with increasing enthusiasm as I realized the shifts in perception whenever my teacher voiced her opinion. I trusted her. However, writing dialogue seemed to me one of the most boring things to do, and, very hesitantly, I opened up my notebook and started to ponder the question, *who am I going to bring together for that tedious task?*

In 2001, I had begun writing a German-language novel which I called *Clara*. It had been sitting on the shelf for quite some time. "What the heck?" I said to myself, and I pragmatically chose four characters from that novel. Mischievously, I thought, they would finally be forced to communicate with each other again. I started the dialogue and, quite frankly, their talk bored me to death.

Enter Anubis.

I do not know whether it was sheer despair, or just a lucky finger hinting to the dark corner over there, but I decided to add a fifth member to the little group—Anubis, the Egyptian God of the Underworld.

Anubis had been worshipped for over three-thousand years; some scholars even say over five-thousand years. He was there long before the Christian-Judaic God had been introduced to the people of the Holy Land, long before those knowledgeable men sat down to write their stories for the Holy Bible and the Talmud.

And he began playing quite a role in my life.

* * *

Some years ago, I stood in a British bookstore and randomly flipped through a book on Egyptian shamanism. My eyes fell on a framed text, and unknowingly, a spiral was about to leap into another holographic universe in my life.

The lines were simple: imagine Anubis standing before you.

I had no time to figure out whether I would be willing to follow this blunt suggestion. He was there, right before me, about twelve feet away. I did not *see* him, to be precise. I *felt* him, as a dark and strong presence. I do not mean *dark* in the sense of *evil*, just dark, like the velvety dark of a night's sky. Since then, darkness has another meaning to me. Darkness can be immensely comforting. In darkness, I can sink down and let myself be held, and even, at times, ravished.

It is the rightful opposite to its much more cherished counterpart, the light.

I must admit, Anubis was not a complete stranger to me. Two years before the bookshop event, a much-revered sound healer had opened the gates of the Egyptian heavens at a workshop and let all his listeners peek around the corner to meet and greet whomever we were inclined to meet. I remember him talking about Anubis in a highly respectful voice. I was not too intrigued at the time. I think I kind of lingered at that gate for quite a while and then decided to return to my mundane life.

Well, Anubis had a pretty strong message for me in that bookstore. *Forget it*, were his words, and although they were not spoken aloud, I could clearly hear them in my head.

Forget it. I knew instantly that those words referred to a relationship I was in at the time: the relationship had reached another peak of misunderstanding and confusion. Its container was close to breaking, and my fingers had virtually cramped from my desperate attempt to hold it together.

Forget it, he had said, and I heard concern in his voice, his love and care, but also his firmness. I opened my arms and let go and surrendered to the vibration of this new truth in me.

That brief encounter with Anubis marked the beginning of a series of exciting explorations. Ever since that day in the bookstore, I have been pondering this question: whose truth had I been responding to? Had I coincidentally tapped into a more intuitive intelligence within me? Or was there really some being out there who had given me his distinct opinion on the matter?

I am still pondering this, to be honest. There is growing certainty, however, that there is a universe *in me*, one that contains all forms and colors and possibly everything else which I can find *out there* as well. It is one of the key questions of my life, and I am continuously exploring those inner and outer worlds.

But back to my creative writing assignment . . .

Adding Anubis to my little group of characters indeed created quite a shift. The dialogue suddenly became intense, and the more I let the words flow through the conscious part of my brain, the more bewildered I became. It was as if Anubis had provided a mirror for the many small and big questions in my life. He was, however, more than just a mirror; he also gave me answers which rang true to my ears.

When I invited him to join my little group of characters, suddenly they all became a lot more alive—and no wonder. The complexity of the plot grew by the second, or better still, by the letter. I grumpily dropped two male characters, reserving the option to use them in a sequel, and concentrated on Clara, my main character, along with Anubis. Then I jumped headlong into those strange conversations.

The dialogues between Anubis and Clara are the basis of this book. The story line anchors those conversations into this mundane, earthly life. I needed that anchor.

The process of writing this book was amazing to me. I learnt at least as much as Clara learnt, and possibly a lot more. The colorful strands of fiction and nonfiction are often tightly interwoven and do not let themselves be distinguished easily. Who knows the difference between reality, or how the so-called ordinary world perceives reality—*maya*—the Vedic synonym for the illusionary character of all things and shamanic dreaming? Gradually, I began to understand what is meant when one says that shamans dream their reality into being. Dreaming is indeed an act of manifestation.

I thank Lynn Andrews from the depth of my heart for her straightforward demand to write a dialogue. Her *abracadabra* is just one proof of her brilliance as a powerful shaman woman. She tapped on that portal and called upon me to put my hand on the knob and turn. When I did, worlds upon worlds opened up.

There were other teachers in my life to whom I am extremely grateful. Tantric teachers. Sound-healing teachers. Trauma-training teachers. I bow down to them, knowing that the most painful lessons were often the most rewarding. Last but not least I would like to thank my husband, who had never doubted that I would manifest my dream of writing this book. Thank you so much for your unconditional love and support and all the good food you prepared while I sat there following my dream!.

Most times, I am very grateful for this process called *life*. For many years, I thought it was all about struggling to survive, and now I gratefully realize that there is joy hovering at the horizon. There are many sidetracks on this journey, but I pray to always return to the path—the Good Red Road, as the native Americans say.

In Liebe, (German for "with love"),

Susanne E. Steinel

Made in the USA
Middletown, DE
03 December 2022

16894936R00130